Algebra 2

with CalcChat® and CalcView®

Practice Workbook and Test Prep

- Extra Practice

- Review & Refresh

- Self-Assessments

- Test Prep

- Post-Course Test

Big Ideas Learning™

Erie, Pennsylvania

Contents

Contents

Contents

Contents

Contents

About the Practice Workbook and Test Prep

Extra Practice

The Extra Practice exercises provide additional practice on the key concepts taught in each section.

Review & Refresh

The Review & Refresh exercises provide students the opportunity to practice prior skills to improve retention.

Self-Assessments

For every section and chapter, students can rate their understanding of the learning targets and success criteria.

Test Prep

Each chapter contains a cumulative test to prepare students for standardized test questions, including multiple choice, multi-select, gridded response, and fill-in-the-blank.

Post-Course Test

The Post-Course Test measures students' understanding of all content in this course. This assessment is designed to prepare students for standardized test questions, including multiple choice, multi-select, gridded response, and fill-in-the-blank.

Name_____ Date_____

1.1 Extra Practice

In Exercises 1 and 2, identify the function family to which *f* belongs. Compare the graph of *f* to the graph of its parent function.

1.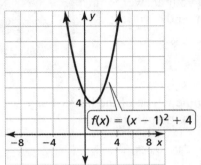

   $f(x) = (x - 1)^2 + 4$

2.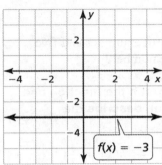

   $f(x) = -3$

In Exercises 3–8, graph the function and its parent function. Then describe the transformation.

3. $f(x) = x - 7$

4. $f(x) = |x| + 1$

5. $h(x) = \left(\frac{1}{2}x\right)^2$

6. $f(x) = -9$

7. $f(x) = \frac{1}{8}x^2$

8. $g(x) = 6|x|$

9. Identify the function family to which the function $f(x) = \frac{1}{3}|-x| + 4$ belongs.

   Then find the domain and range. Use technology to verify your answer.

10. The table shows the distance a bicyclist rides in his first team relay competition. What type of function can be used to model the data? If the bicyclist's teammate rides at the same pace but leaves 1 hour later, what type of transformation does this represent? Explain.

Time (hours), *x*	1	2	3	4
Distance (miles), *y*	12	24	36	48

11. Use the values −1, 1, and 2 to complete each function so their graphs intersect the *x*-axis. Explain your reasoning.

    a. $f(x) = -2x \text{———} + 3$

    b. $f(x) = 2x^2 - \text{———}$

    c. $f(x) = \text{———} |x - 4| + 2$

1.1 Review & Refresh

1. Tell whether $(7, -4)$ is a solution of $y \geq 5 - x$.

2. The sum of one-fourth a number and five is three. What is the number?

In Exercises 3 and 4, graph the function and its parent function. Then describe the transformation.

3. $g(x) = |x + 3|$ 4. $h(x) = \frac{4}{3}x$

5. Solve $3\sqrt{x} - 4 = 2$.

6. Tell whether the table of values represents a *linear*, an *exponential*, or a *quadratic* function.

x	0	1	2	3	4
y	5	15	45	135	405

7. Find the volume of the cone. Round your answer to the nearest tenth.

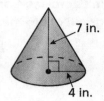
7 in.
4 in.

8. Determine which of the lines, if any, are parallel or perpendicular.

Line *a*: $3y - x = 2$

Line *b*: $y = 3x - 2$

Line *c*: $-6x + 2y = 5$

9. The inaugural attendance at an annual music festival is 60,000 people. The attendance increases by 7% each year. Find the attendance at the festival in the fifth year.

In Exercises 10 and 11, factor the polynomial completely.

10. $x^2 - 20x + 100$ 11. $3x^3 - 12x$

1.1 Self-Assessment

Use the scale to rate your understanding of the learning target and the success criteria.

| 1 | I do not understand. | 2 | I can do it with help. | 3 | I can do it on my own. | 4 | I can teach someone else. |

	Rating	Date
1.1 Parent Functions and Transformations		
Learning Target: Graph and describe transformations of functions.	1 2 3 4	
I can identify the function family to which a function belongs.	1 2 3 4	
I can graph transformations of functions.	1 2 3 4	
I can explain how translations, reflections, stretches, and shrinks affect graphs of functions.	1 2 3 4	

Name_____ Date_____

In Exercises 1–10, write a function *g* whose graph represents the indicated transformation of the graph of *f*. Use technology to check your answer.

1. $f(x) = x + 7$; translation 5 units right

2. $f(x) = \left|\frac{1}{3}x\right|$; translation 2 units left

3. $f(x) = -2x + 2$; translation 7 units down

4. $f(x) = -|x + 9| - 1$; translation 6 units up

5. $f(x) = \frac{1}{2}x + 8$; reflection in the x-axis

6. $f(x) = 4 + |x + 1|$; reflection in the y-axis

7. $f(x) = -5x$; vertical shrink by a factor of $\frac{1}{5}$

8. $f(x) = |x + 3| + 2$; vertical stretch by a factor of 4

9. $f(x) = 3x - 9$; horizontal stretch by a factor of 6

10. $f(x) = -|8x| - 4$; vertical shrink by a factor of $\frac{1}{4}$

11. Consider the function $f(x) = x$. Write a function g whose graph represents a reflection in the x-axis followed by a horizontal stretch by a factor of 3 and a translation 5 units down of the graph of f.

12. You make fluid-art paintings to sell. Your revenue (in dollars) for x paintings is given by $f(x) = 25x$ and your profit is $5 more than 30% of the revenue. What is your profit for 12 paintings?

13. Describe the transformations of the graph of the parent absolute value function to obtain the graph of $g(x) = -\frac{1}{2}|x| - 6$. Explain your reasoning.

14. Complete the function $g(x) = \underline{\quad}|x - \underline{\quad}| + \underline{\quad}$ so that g is a reflection in the x-axis followed by a translation three units right and two units down of the graph of $f(x) = 3|x - 1| + 8$. Explain your reasoning.

Name _____ Date _____

1.2 Review & Refresh

In Exercises 1 and 2, evaluate the function for the given value of x.

1. $f(x) = 5x - 9$; $x = 4$

2. $f(x) = -4x + 6$; $x = -7$

3. Make a scatter plot of the data. Then describe the relationship between the data.

x	f(x)
1	5
2	3
3	2
4	2
5	1

4. Identify the function family to which g belongs. Compare the graph of the function to the graph of its parent function.

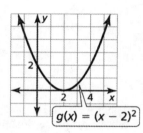
$g(x) = (x - 2)^2$

5. The function $f(x) = 500x - 10,000$ represents the elevation (in feet) of a submersible x minutes after the submersible begins to ascend.

   a. Graph the function and find its domain and range.

   b. Interpret the slope and the intercepts of the graph.

In Exercises 6 and 7, write a function g whose graph represents the indicated transformations of the graph of f.

6. $f(x) = x$; translation 5 units down and a horizontal shrink by a factor of $\frac{1}{6}$

7. $f(x) = |x|$; reflection in the x-axis and a vertical shrink by a factor of $\frac{1}{3}$ followed by a translation 8 units up and 2 units left

1.2 Self-Assessment

Use the scale to rate your understanding of the learning target and the success criteria.

| 1 | I do not understand. | 2 | I can do it with help. | 3 | I can do it on my own. | 4 | I can teach someone else. |

	Rating	Date
1.2 Transformations of Linear and Absolute Value Functions		
Learning Target: Write functions that represent transformations of functions.	1 2 3 4	
I can write functions that represent transformations of linear functions.	1 2 3 4	
I can write functions that represent transformations of absolute value functions.	1 2 3 4	

Name_____ Date_____

1.3 Extra Practice

In Exercises 1 and 2, use the graph to write an equation of the line and interpret the slope.

1.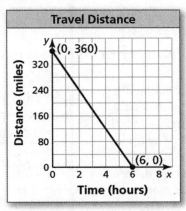

2.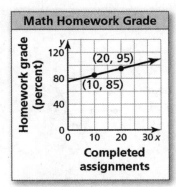

3. The cost to park in a parking garage in Chicago is represented by the equation $y = 15x + 20$ where y is the total cost (in dollars) and x is the time (in hours). The table shows the total cost to park in a parking garage in Denver. Which city's parking garage charges more per hour and by how much more? After how many hours would parking in both cities cost the same?

Hours, x	Cost, y
2	$43
3	$51
4	$59
5	$67

4. Determine whether the data show a linear relationship. If so, write an equation of a line of fit. Then estimate y when $x = 8$ and explain its meaning in the context of the situation.

Game, x	1	3	5	7	9
Number of people in attendance, y	273	297	321	336	350

In Exercises 5 and 6, use technology to find an equation of the line of best fit for the data. Identify and interpret the correlation coefficient.

5.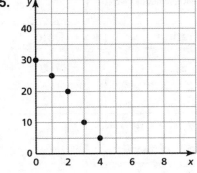

6.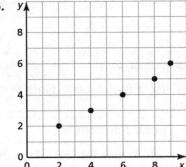

1.3 Review & Refresh

1. Solve the system using any method. Explain your choice of method.

   $10x - 4y = 6$

   $5x - 2y = 3$

2. Write a system of linear inequalities represented by the graph.

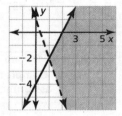

3. Solve the literal equation $w + 2x = 5x + 6y - 9$ for x.

4. What percent of 50 is 18?

In Exercises 5 and 6, graph the function and its parent function. Then describe the transformation.

5. $f(x) = -1.5$

6. $b(x) = -|x - 3| + 2$

In Exercises 7 and 8, find the sum or difference.

7. $(x^2 - 3x + 12) + (6x^2 - 2x - 3)$

8. $(-2n^3 + 5n^2 - 8n) - (9n^2 + 6n - 1)$

9. Two music streaming service providers charge a set-up fee plus a monthly service fee. The table shows the total costs (in dollars) for different numbers of months at Company A. The total cost y (in dollars) for x months of service at Company B is represented by $y = 12x + 15$. Which company charges less per month? After how many months of service are the total costs the same?

Company A	
Months, x	Total cost, y
2	$49
3	$59
4	$69
5	$79
6	$89

10. Let $f(x) = -5|x - 1|$. Write a function g whose graph is a vertical shrink by a factor of $\frac{1}{3}$ of the graph of f.

1.3 Self-Assessment

Use the scale to rate your understanding of the learning target and the success criteria.

| 1 | I do not understand. | | 2 | I can do it with help. | | 3 | I can do it on my own. | | 4 | I can teach someone else. |

	Rating	Date
1.3 Modeling with Linear Functions		
Learning Target: Use linear functions to model and analyze real-life situations.	1 2 3 4	
I can write equations of linear functions.	1 2 3 4	
I can compare linear equations to solve real-life problems.	1 2 3 4	
I can determine a line of best fit.	1 2 3 4	

Name_____ Date_____

1.4 Extra Practice

In Exercises 1–3, solve the system using the elimination method.

1. $x + 2y - 3z = 11$
   $2x + y - 2z = 9$
   $4x + 3y + z = 16$

2. $x - y + 3z = 19$
   $-2x + 2y - 6z = 9$
   $3x + 5y + 2z = 3$

3. $x + y - z = -9$
   $2x - 3y + 2z = 13$
   $3x - 5y - 6z = -15$

In Exercises 4–6, solve the system of linear equations using the substitution method.

4. $x + y + z = 4$
   $x + y - z = 4$
   $3x + 3y + z = 12$

5. $2x + 3y - z = 9$
   $x - 3y + z = -6$
   $3x + y - 4z = 31$

6. $x + 2y - 5z = -12$
   $2x + 2y - 3z = -2$
   $3x - 4y - z = 11$

7. You find $6.60 on the ground at school, all in nickels, dimes, and quarters. You have twice as many quarters as dimes and 42 coins in all. How many of each type of coin do you have?

8. If $\angle A$ is three times as large as $\angle B$, and $\angle B$ is 30° smaller than $\angle C$, what are the measures of angles A, B, and C?

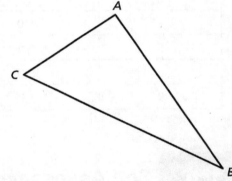

9. Find the values of a, b, and c so that the linear system shown has $(3, -2, 1)$ as its only solution. Explain your reasoning.

   $3x + 2y - 7z = a$
   $x + 3y + z = b$
   $4x - 2y - z = c$

10. Determine which arrangement(s) of the integers -1, 2, and -3 produce a linear system with a solution that consists of only integers. Justify your answer.

    $2x + 3y + z = 4$
    ____$x +$ ____$y +$ ____$z = -11$
    $x + 2y - 7z = -35$

Name _____   Date _____

In Exercises 1 and 2, write a function g described by the given transformation of $f(x) = |x| - 7$.

1. translation 4 units to the right

2. vertical shrink by a factor of $\frac{1}{7}$

3. Find $(2m - 9)^2$.

4. Solve $|3 + 2h| - 8 > -1$. Graph the solution.

5. The table shows the total cost (in dollars) of a television streaming service after x months. What type of function can you use to model the data? Estimate the total cost after 1 year.

Time (months), x	Total cost (dollars), y
0	0
2	30
5	75
6	90
9	135

6. Use the graph to write an equation of the line and interpret the slope.

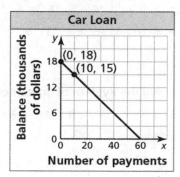

Car Loan

7. $b^{-5} \cdot b^3$

8. $\left(\dfrac{z^4}{5}\right)^{-2}$

9. Find the value of x.

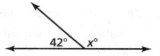

$42°$ $x°$

10. Solve the system.

$$-x + 3y + z = -6$$
$$3x - 9y - 3z = -18$$
$$x = 7 - y$$

Use the scale to rate your understanding of the learning target and the success criteria.

1 I do not understand.   **2** I can do it with help.   **3** I can do it on my own.   **4** I can teach someone else.

	Rating	Date
1.4 Solving Linear Systems		
Learning Target: Solve linear systems in three variables.	1 2 3 4	
I can visualize solutions of linear systems in three variables.	1 2 3 4	
I can solve linear systems in three variables algebraically.	1 2 3 4	
I can solve real-life problems using systems of equations in three variables.	1 2 3 4	

Name_____ Date _____

Chapter Self-Assessment

Use the scale to rate your understanding of the learning target and the success criteria.

1 I do not understand.   **2** I can do it with help.   **3** I can do it on my own.   **4** I can teach someone else.

	Rating	Date
Chapter 1 Linear Functions		
Learning Target: Understand linear functions.	1 2 3 4	
I can identify parent functions and transformations.	1 2 3 4	
I can describe transformations of parent functions.	1 2 3 4	
I can model with linear functions.	1 2 3 4	
I can solve linear systems.	1 2 3 4	
1.1 Parent Functions and Transformations		
Learning Target: Graph and describe transformations of functions.	1 2 3 4	
I can identify the function family to which a function belongs.	1 2 3 4	
I can graph transformations of functions.	1 2 3 4	
I can explain how translations, reflections, stretches, and shrinks affect graphs of functions.	1 2 3 4	
1.2 Transformations of Linear and Absolute Value Functions		
Learning Target: Write functions that represent transformations of functions.	1 2 3 4	
I can write functions that represent transformations of linear functions.	1 2 3 4	
I can write functions that represent transformations of absolute value functions.	1 2 3 4	
1.3 Modeling with Linear Functions		
Learning Target: Use linear functions to model and analyze real-life situations.	1 2 3 4	
I can write equations of linear functions.	1 2 3 4	
I can compare linear equations to solve real-life problems.	1 2 3 4	
I can determine a line of best fit.	1 2 3 4	

Chapter 1 Chapter Self-Assessment (continued)

	Rating	Date
1.4 Solving Linear Systems		
Learning Target: Solve linear systems in three variables.	1 2 3 4	
I can visualize solutions of linear systems in three variables.	1 2 3 4	
I can solve linear systems in three variables algebraically.	1 2 3 4	
I can solve real-life problems using systems of equations in three variables.	1 2 3 4	

Name_____ Date_____

Chapter 1 — Test Prep

1. Which expression is equivalent to $(5 - 3m) + (6m - 8m^2 + 7)$?

- Ⓐ $8m^2 + 3m + 12$
- Ⓑ $8m^2 - 3m + 12$
- Ⓒ $-8m^2 + 3m + 12$
- Ⓓ $-8m^2 - 3m + 12$

2. Which graph represents the solution of $6 + 3y < 9$ *or* $4y > 3y + 2$?

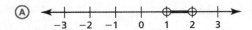

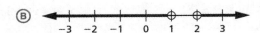

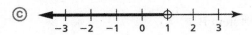

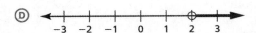

3. Write an equation of the line.

_____

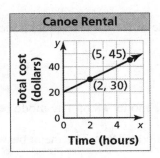

Canoe Rental

4. Solve $2n - 3 = 5n + 6$.

$n =$

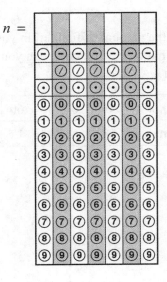

5. Evaluate $(25)^{-1/2}$.

Chapter 1 Test Prep (continued)

6. Which of the following systems has infinitely many solutions?

System A

$-x - y - 2z = 9$

$-2x + 2y - 4z = 18$

$x - y + z = 5$

System B

$x + y + z = 9$

$2x - 3y + 4z = 7$

$x - 4y + 3z = -2$

Ⓐ System A

Ⓑ System B

Ⓒ both

Ⓓ neither

7. Find the mean, median, and mode of the data set. Which measure of center best represents the data?

50.4, 16.2, 24.6, 18.6, 23.1, 18.6

Ⓐ mean: 25.25; median: 20.85; mode: 18.6; The mode best describes the data.

Ⓑ mean: 30.3; median: 21.6; mode: 18.6; The mean best describes the data.

Ⓒ mean: 25.25; median: 20.85; mode: 18.6; The median best describes the data.

Ⓓ mean: 20.25; median: 23.1; mode: 18.6; The median best describes the data.

8. Select all the functions that belong in the same function family as $f(x) = 6 - x^2$.

Ⓐ $g(x) = -\frac{1}{3}x^2 + 4x - 9$

Ⓑ $h(x) = 3 - |2x|$

Ⓒ $k(x) = 2 - 4$

Ⓓ $m(x) = 2(x - 1)^2 - 3$

Ⓔ $n(x) = x(x + 5)$

9. The table shows the amount of fuel left in your RV while driving. What type of function can you use to model the data?

Time (minutes), x	0	20	40	60	80
Fuel left (gallons), y	18	16	14	12	10

Ⓐ constant

Ⓑ linear

Ⓒ absolute value

Ⓓ quadratic

Chapter 1 Test Prep (continued)

10. The function $c = 125 + 0.25m$ represents the cost c (in dollars) of renting a car, where m is the number of miles you drive the rental car. How many miles will a customer have to drive for the cost to be $168.75?

miles

11. A local grocery store makes a 9-pound mixture of trail mix. The trail mix contains raisins, sunflower seeds, and chocolate-covered peanuts. The raisins cost $2 per pound, the sunflower seeds cost $1 per pound, and the chocolate-covered peanuts cost $1.50 per pound. The mixture calls for twice as many raisins as sunflower seeds. The total cost of the mixture is $14.50. How much of each ingredient did the store use?

Ⓐ 2 pounds raisins, 3 pounds sunflower seeds, 4 pounds chocolate-covered peanuts

Ⓑ 3 pounds raisins, 4 pounds sunflower seeds, 2 pounds chocolate-covered peanuts

Ⓒ 4 pounds raisins, 2 pounds sunflower seeds, 3 pounds chocolate-covered peanuts

Ⓓ 4.4 pounds raisins, 2.4 pounds sunflower seeds, 2.2 pounds chocolate-covered peanuts

12. Let $f(x) = \frac{2}{3}x^2 + 2$. The graph of g is a translation 5 units down, followed by a vertical stretch by a factor of 3 of the graph of f. Which function represents g?

Ⓐ $g(x) = 2x^2 - 9$

Ⓑ $g(x) = 2x^2 + 21$

Ⓒ $g(x) = 2x^2 - 3$

Ⓓ $g(x) = 9x^2 - 3$

Chapter 1

Test Prep (continued)

13. Select all the ways you can describe the transformation from the graph of the parent linear function to the graph of $g(x) = x + 5$.

    Ⓐ The graph of g is a vertical translation 5 units down of the graph of the parent linear function.

    Ⓑ The graph of g is a horizontal translation 5 units left of the graph of the parent linear function.

    Ⓒ The graph of g is a horizontal translation 5 units right of the graph of the parent linear function.

    Ⓓ The graph of g is a vertical translation 5 units up of the graph of the parent linear function.

14. What is the value of y when $x = 3\sqrt{7}$ and $4x = \sqrt{7y}$?

    $y =$

15. The graph of h is a reflection in the x-axis followed by a translation two units left and three units down of the graph of $f(x) = \frac{1}{2}|x + 3| + 4$. Which of the following functions represents the function h?

    Ⓐ $h(x) = -\frac{1}{2}|x + 1| - 7$

    Ⓑ $h(x) = -\frac{1}{2}|x + 1| + 1$

    Ⓒ $h(x) = -\frac{1}{2}|x + 5| - 7$

    Ⓓ $h(x) = -\frac{1}{2}|x + 5| + 1$

Name_____ Date_____

In Exercises 1–6, describe the transformation of $f(x) = x^2$ represented by g. Then graph each function.

1. $g(x) = x^2 + 4$

2. $g(x) = x^2 - 7$

3. $g(x) = (x - 1)^2 - 3$

4. $g(x) = (-4x)^2$

5. $g(x) = \frac{1}{3}x^2 - 6$

6. $g(x) = -(x + 9)^2$

In Exercises 7–10, write a rule for g described by the transformations of the graph of f. Then identify the vertex.

7. $f(x) = x^2$; vertical stretch by a factor of 5 and a reflection in the x-axis, followed by a translation 3 units down

8. $f(x) = x^2$; vertical shrink by a factor of $\frac{1}{2}$ and a reflection in the y-axis, followed by a translation 4 units left

9. $f(x) = 9x^2 - 3$; horizontal stretch by a factor of 3 and a translation 4 units up, followed by a reflection in the y-axis

10. $f(x) = (x - 12)^2 + 1$; horizontal shrink by a factor of $\frac{1}{4}$ and a translation 8 units down, followed by a reflection in the x-axis

11. Let $f(x) = (x - 1)^2 - 2$. Describe a combination of different types of transformations of f that result in the original function.

Name _____ Date _____

2.1 Review & Refresh

1. Solve the system.

   $2x + 8y + 9z = -8$

   $x - 3y - z = 7$

   $-x + 2z = -9$

2. Let the graph of g be a translation 2 units right and 3 units up, followed by a vertical shrink by a factor of $\frac{1}{3}$ of the graph of $f(x) = 6(x + 1)^2$. Write a rule for g and identify the vertex.

3. Factor $4x^3 + 28x^2$.

4. Use the intercepts to graph the equation $2x - 4y = 8$.

5. A line of best fit has a correlation coefficient of about -0.987. What can you conclude about the slope of the line?

6. Describe the transformation of $f(x) = x^2$ represented by g.

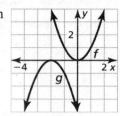

7. Display the data in a histogram. Describe the shape of the distribution.

Exam score	Frequency
61–70	2
71–80	4
81–90	5
91–100	7

8. The cost (in dollars) of x T-shirts at a store's regular price is modeled by the function $f(x) = 10x$. The cost of x T-shirts during a sale is $6 less than 75% of the cost at regular price. What is the cost of five T-shirts during the sale?

2.1 Self-Assessment

Use the scale to rate your understanding of the learning target and the success criteria.

| 1 | I do not understand. | 2 | I can do it with help. | 3 | I can do it on my own. | 4 | I can teach someone else. |

	Rating	Date
2.1 Transformations of Quadratic Functions		
Learning Target: Describe and graph transformations of quadratic functions.	1 2 3 4	
I can describe transformations of quadratic functions.	1 2 3 4	
I can graph transformations of quadratic functions.	1 2 3 4	
I can write functions that represent transformations of quadratic functions.	1 2 3 4	

Name_____ Date _____

2.2 Extra Practice

In Exercises 1–3, graph the function. Label the vertex and axis of symmetry.

1. $f(x) = (x + 1)^2$

2. $y = -2(x - 4)^2 - 5$

3. $t(x) = \frac{3}{2}x^2 - 3x - 1$

In Exercises 4–6, find the minimum value or maximum value of the function. Find the domain and range of the function, and when the function is increasing and decreasing.

4. $y = -4x^2 + 8x + 3$

5. $k(x) = 5x^2 + 20x$

6. $h(x) = \frac{1}{2}x^2 - 4x + 3$

In Exercises 7 and 8, graph the function. Label the x-intercept(s), vertex, and axis of symmetry.

7. $f(x) = 4(x + 4)(x - 3)$

8. $f(x) = -7x(x - 6)$

9. The height (in feet) of a dolphin above the water is given by $f(t) = -16t(t - 1.5)$, where t is the time (in seconds) since the dolphin jumped out of the water. The graph shows the path of a second dolphin that jumps out of the water. Which dolphin jumps higher? Which dolphin remains in the air longer? Justify your answer.

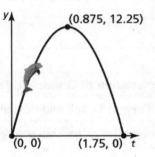

10. An archeologist has $2k$ meters of rope to mark a rectangular dig site. What is the maximum area of the dig site in terms of k?

Name_____ Date _____

2.2 Review & Refresh

In Exercises 1 and 2, solve the equation.

1. $\sqrt{9x} + 1 = 0$ **2.** $\sqrt{4x + 12} = x$

3. Solve $\dfrac{2}{9} = \dfrac{-14}{x}$.

4. Describe the transformation of $f(x) = x^2$ represented by g.

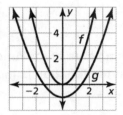

5. The table shows the depth y (in centimeters) of water filling a bathtub after x minutes. Do the data show a linear relationship? If so, write an equation of a line of fit and use it to estimate the depth of the bathtub after 10 minutes.

Minutes, x	0	2	4	6	8
Depth (centimeters), y	6	8	11	14	17

6. Solve $|2x - 5| = 3|x + 5|$.

In Exercises 7 and 8, graph the function. Label the x-intercept(s), vertex, and axis of symmetry.

7. $g(x) = 2(x + 3)(x - 1)$

8. $f(x) = -0.1x(x - 2)$

9. Find the volume of the pyramid.

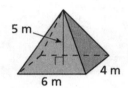

10. Determine whether $y = 0.8(1.15)^t$ represents *exponential growth* or *exponential decay*. Identify the percent rate of change.

11. Solve $-3 < \frac{1}{3}(n + 6) \le 2$. Graph the solution.

2.2 Self-Assessment

Use the scale to rate your understanding of the learning target and the success criteria.

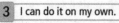

| 1 | I do not understand. | 2 | I can do it with help. | 3 | I can do it on my own. | 4 | I can teach someone else. |

	Rating	Date
2.2 Characteristics of Quadratic Functions		
Learning Target: Graph and describe quadratic functions.	1 2 3 4	
I can use properties of parabolas to graph quadratic functions.	1 2 3 4	
I can identify characteristics of quadratic functions and their graphs.	1 2 3 4	
I can use characteristics of quadratic functions to solve real-life problems.	1 2 3 4	

Name_____ Date _____

2.3 Extra Practice

In Exercises 1 and 2, write an equation of the parabola.

1. focus: $(0, -8)$

   directrix: $y = 8$

2. vertex: $(0, 0)$

   focus: $(0, 1)$

In Exercises 3–5, identify the focus, directrix, and axis of symmetry of the parabola. Graph the equation.

3. $x = \frac{1}{6}y^2$

4. $x^2 = -2y$

5. $-5x + \frac{1}{3}y^2 = 0$

In Exercises 6–9, write an equation of the parabola.

6.
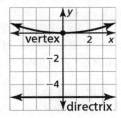

7.
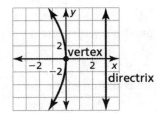

8.
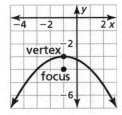

9.
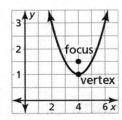

In Exercises 10 and 11, write an equation of the parabola with the given characteristics.

10. directrix: $y = 1$

    vertex: $(6, 5)$

11. focus: $\left(-\frac{15}{2}, -8\right)$

    directrix: $x = -\frac{13}{2}$

12. The cross section of a parabolic sound reflector at the Olympics has a diameter of 20 inches and is 25 inches deep. Write an equation that represents the cross section of the reflector with its vertex at $(0, 0)$ and its focus to the left of the vertex.

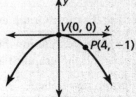

13. The distance from point P to the directrix is 5 units. Write an equation of the parabola.

2.3 Review & Refresh

1. Write an equation of the line that passes through $(-1, -10)$ and $(6, 18)$.

2. Graph $y \le \frac{2}{3}x + 2$.

3. The graph of square root function g is shown. Compare the average rate of change of $h(x) = \sqrt[3]{2x}$ to the average rate of change of g over the interval $x = 0$ to $x = 4$.

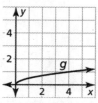

4. Write an equation of a parabola with vertex $(-1, -3)$ and focus $(1, 0)$.

5. Use technology to find an equation of the line of best fit for the data.

x	0	2	4	6	7
y	7	4	2	1	0

6. Determine whether the table represents a *linear* or *nonlinear* function. Explain.

x	-2	-1	1	2	3
y	3	6	24	48	96

7. Let the graph of g be a translation 3 units down followed by a reflection in the x-axis and a vertical shrink by a factor of $\frac{1}{3}$ of the graph of $f(x) = x^2$. Write a rule for g and identify the vertex.

8. Solve $2(4x - 7) = 6x + 2$.

9. You have $0.97 in quarters, nickels, and pennies. You have 17 coins in all. You have four times as many pennies as quarters. How many of each type of coin do you have?

10. Identify the focus, directrix, and axis of symmetry of $2x = y^2$. Graph the equation.

2.3 Self-Assessment

Use the scale to rate your understanding of the learning target and the success criteria.

| 1 | I do not understand. | 2 | I can do it with help. | 3 | I can do it on my own. | 4 | I can teach someone else. |

	Rating	Date
2.3 Focus of a Parabola		
Learning Target: Graph and write equations of parabolas.	1 2 3 4	
I can explain the relationships among the focus, the directrix, and the graph of a parabola.	1 2 3 4	
I can graph parabolas.	1 2 3 4	
I can write equations of parabolas.	1 2 3 4	

2.4 Extra Practice

In Exercises 1 and 2, write an equation of the parabola in vertex form.

1.

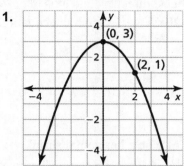

2. passes through $(-3, 0)$ and has vertex $(-1, -8)$

In Exercises 3 and 4, write an equation of the parabola in intercept form.

3.

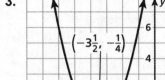

4. x-intercepts of 7 and 10; passes through $(-2, 27)$

5. The table shows a university's budget (in millions of dollars) over a 10-year period, where $x = 0$ represents the first year in the 10-year period. Write a function that models the data. Use the model to predict when the budget of the university is \$300,000,000.00.

Years, x	0	1	2	3	4	5	6	7	8	9
Budget, y	65	32	22	40	65	92	114	128	140	150

6. Analyze the differences in the outputs to determine whether the data are *linear*, *quadratic*, or *neither*. Explain. If the data are linear or quadratic, write a function that models the data.

Time (seconds), x	1	2	3	4	5	6
Distance (feet), y	424	416	376	304	200	64

7. The table shows the number of tiles in each figure. Verify that the data show a quadratic relationship. Predict the number of tiles in the 15th figure.

Figure	1	2	3	4
Number of tiles	5	8	13	20

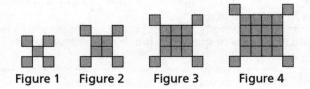

Figure 1   Figure 2   Figure 3   Figure 4

Name _____ Date _____

In Exercises 1 and 2, factor the polynomial.

1. $2x^2 - 26x + 80$ **2.** $x^2 + 5x - 84$

3. The table shows the heights y (in feet) of a ball x seconds after it is kicked. Write an equation for the path of the ball. Find the maximum height of the ball.

Time, x	0	0.5	1	1.5
Height, y	0	10	12	6

4. Determine whether the graph represents a function. Explain.

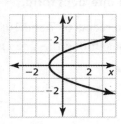

5. Graph $h(x) = 4x^2 + 16x + 7$. Label the vertex and axis of symmetry.

6. Identify the focus, directrix, and axis of symmetry of $20x = y^2$. Graph the equation.

7. Let the graph of g be a horizontal shrink by a factor of $\frac{1}{3}$, followed by a translation 6 units down and 5 units left of the graph of $f(x) = (4x - 3)^2 + 7$. Write a rule for g and identify the vertex.

8. Solve $-\frac{q}{4} \leq 1$. Graph the solution.

9. Determine whether the table represents a *linear* or an *exponential* function. Explain.

x	−1	0	1	2	3
y	$\frac{1}{2}$	3	18	108	648

Use the scale to rate your understanding of the learning target and the success criteria.

| 1 | I do not understand. | 2 | I can do it with help. | 3 | I can do it on my own. | 4 | I can teach someone else. |

	Rating	Date
2.4 Modeling with Quadratic Functions		
Learning Target: Write equations of quadratic functions using given characteristics.	1 2 3 4	
I can write equations of quadratic functions using vertices, points, and x-intercepts.	1 2 3 4	
I can write quadratic equations to model data sets.	1 2 3 4	
I can use technology to find a quadratic model for a set of data.	1 2 3 4	

Name_____ Date_____

Chapter 2 — Chapter Self-Assessment

Use the scale to rate your understanding of the learning target and the success criteria.

| 1 | I do not understand. | 2 | I can do it with help. | 3 | I can do it on my own. | 4 | I can teach someone else. |

	Rating	Date
Chapter 2 Quadratic Functions		
Learning Target: Understand quadratic functions.	1 2 3 4	
I can describe transformations of quadratic functions.	1 2 3 4	
I can identify characteristics of quadratic functions.	1 2 3 4	
I can write equations of parabolas.	1 2 3 4	
I can model with quadratic functions.	1 2 3 4	
2.1 Transformations of Quadratic Functions		
Learning Target: Describe and graph transformations of quadratic functions.	1 2 3 4	
I can describe transformations of quadratic functions.	1 2 3 4	
I can graph transformations of quadratic functions.	1 2 3 4	
I can write functions that represent transformations of quadratic functions.	1 2 3 4	
2.2 Characteristics of Quadratic Functions		
Learning Target: Graph and describe quadratic functions.	1 2 3 4	
I can use properties of parabolas to graph quadratic functions.	1 2 3 4	
I can identify characteristics of quadratic functions and their graphs.	1 2 3 4	
I can use characteristics of quadratic functions to solve real-life problems.	1 2 3 4	
2.3 Focus of a Parabola		
Learning Target: Graph and write equations of parabolas.	1 2 3 4	
I can explain the relationships among the focus, the directrix, and the graph of a parabola.	1 2 3 4	
I can graph parabolas.	1 2 3 4	
I can write equations of parabolas.	1 2 3 4	

Chapter 2 — Chapter Self-Assessment (continued)

	Rating	Date
2.4 Modeling with Quadratic Functions		
Learning Target: Write equations of quadratic functions using given characteristics.	1 2 3 4	
I can write equations of quadratic functions using vertices, points, and x-intercepts.	1 2 3 4	
I can write quadratic equations to model data sets.	1 2 3 4	
I can use technology to find a quadratic model for a set of data.	1 2 3 4	

Name_____ Date_____

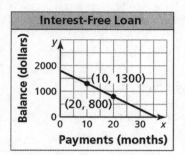 **Test Prep**

Chapter 2

1. The graph shows the balance of an interest-free loan after x monthly payments. What is the balance of the account after 24 payments?

Interest-Free Loan

(10, 1300)
(20, 800)

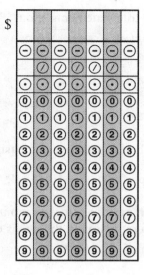

2. Which of the following equations does *not* represent the parabola?

Ⓐ $y = 0.5(x + 4.5)^2 - 1$

Ⓑ $y = 0.5(x - 2)(x + 4)$

Ⓒ $y = 0.5(x + 1)^2 - 4.5$

Ⓓ $y = 0.5x^2 + x - 4$

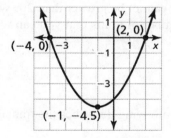

3. Which equation represents the line that passes through $(2, 6)$ and has a slope of -4?

Ⓐ $y - 2 = -4(x - 6)$

Ⓑ $y - 6 = -4(x - 2)$

Ⓒ $y + 2 = -4(x + 6)$

Ⓓ $y - 6 = -4(x + 2)$

4. The graph of which function has the same axis of symmetry as the graph of $y = x^2 + 4x + 5$?

Ⓐ $y = x^2 - 2x - 6$

Ⓑ $y = x^2 - 4x + 2$

Ⓒ $y = 4x^2 + 8x + 5$

Ⓓ $y = -2x^2 - 8x - 1$

Chapter 2

Test Prep (continued)

5. Select all the true statements about the function $k(x) = -\sqrt{x + 6}$.

   Ⓐ The domain of k is $x \geq 6$.

   Ⓑ The range of k is $y \leq 0$.

   Ⓒ The graph of k is always decreasing.

   Ⓓ The value of k at $x = 10$ is -4.

   Ⓔ The graph of k is a translation 6 units left and a reflection in the x-axis of the graph of $f(x) = \sqrt{x}$.

6. Select all the true statements about the graph of $y = -\frac{1}{36}(x - 3)^2 - 2$.

   Ⓐ The vertex is $(3, -2)$.

   Ⓑ The focus is $(3, -11)$.

   Ⓒ The axis of symmetry is $x = 3$.

   Ⓓ The directrix is $y = 11$.

7. You work at a shoe store and a painting company. You must work no more than 6 hours per week at the shoe store, and the total number of hours you work at both jobs in a week cannot be greater than 20. Write a system of linear inequalities that models the number of hours that you can work at each location in a week.

_____

8. Which of the following describes the transformation from the graph of $f(x) = x^2$ to the graph of $h(x) = \left(\frac{1}{4}x\right)^2 + 5$?

   Ⓐ The graph of h is a vertical stretch by a factor of 4, followed by a translation 5 units up of the graph of f.

   Ⓑ The graph of h is a horizontal stretch by a factor of 4, followed by a translation 5 units up of the graph of f.

   Ⓒ The graph of h is a vertical shrink by a factor of $\frac{1}{4}$, followed by a translation 5 units up of the graph of f.

   Ⓓ The graph of h is a horizontal shrink by a factor of $\frac{1}{4}$, followed by a translation 5 units up of the graph of f.

Chapter 2 Test Prep (continued)

9. Your class council determined that its profit from the upcoming homecoming dance is directly related to the ticket price for the dance. Looking at past dances, the council determined that the profit p can be modeled by the function $p(t) = -12t^2 + 480t + 30$, where t represents the price of each ticket. What should be the price of a ticket to the homecoming dance to maximize the council's profit?

10. Let the graph of g be a vertical shrink by a factor of $\frac{1}{3}$ and a translation 4 units right, followed by a reflection in the x-axis of the graph of $f(x) = 3(x + 2)^2 - 9$. Which is a rule for g?

Ⓐ $g(x) = -(x - 2)^2 - 9$

Ⓑ $g(x) = -(x + 6)^2 + 3$

Ⓒ $g(x) = -(x - 2)^2 + 3$

Ⓓ $g(x) = -(x - 2)^2 - 3$

11. Which is a recursive rule for $a_n = 2(3)^{n-1}$?

Ⓐ $a_1 = 2, a_n = 3a_{n-1}$

Ⓑ $a_1 = 6, a_n = 3a_{n-1}$

Ⓒ $a_1 = 3, a_n = 2a_{n-1}$

Ⓓ $a_1 = 6, a_n = 2a_{n-1}$

12. Which of the following values of x and y does *not* make the relation a function?

$(-3, 2), (-1, 5), (0, -1), (4, 6)$

Ⓐ $x = -2, y = 6$

Ⓑ $x = -1, y = 2$

Ⓒ $x = 5, y = -1$

Ⓓ $x = 6, y = -3$

13. The table shows the heights y of a snowboarder x seconds after jumping off a ramp. When is the snowboarder 3 feet above the ground?

Time (seconds), x	0	0.25	0.5	0.75	1
Height (feet), y	10	15	18	19	18

seconds

14. The length of a rectangle is 1 meter more than three times its width. The value of the area of the rectangle (in square meters) is 4 more than the value of the perimeter (in meters). What is the width?

    Ⓐ 10 meters

    Ⓑ 6 meters

    Ⓒ 3 meters

    Ⓓ 2 meters

15. The distance from point P to the directrix is 8 units. Write an equation of the parabola.

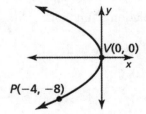

$P(-4, -8)$ $V(0, 0)$

_____

16. For which values of c does $8x^2 + 6x + 3c = 0$ have no real solution?

    Ⓐ $c > \frac{3}{8}$

    Ⓑ $c = \frac{3}{8}$

    Ⓒ $c \neq \frac{3}{8}$

    Ⓓ $c < \frac{3}{8}$

Name_____ Date _____

3.1 Extra Practice

In Exercises 1–3, solve the equation by graphing.

1. $x^2 - 11x + 24 = 0$

2. $13 = -x^2 - 12$

3. $12x^2 = 5x + 2$

In Exercises 4–6, solve the equation using square roots.

4. $t^2 = 400$

5. $(2k + 3)^2 - 19 = 81$

6. $\frac{1}{7}p^2 = \frac{5}{7}p^2 - 20$

In Exercises 7–9, solve the equation by factoring.

7. $0 = x^2 - 12x + 36$

8. $x^2 = 14x - 40$

9. $5x^2 + 5x - 1 = -x^2 + 4x$

In Exercises 10–12, find the zero(s) of the function.

10. $g(x) = x^2 - 13x$

11. $q(x) = 3x^2 + 15x - 72$

12. $k(x) = 12x^2 + 4x - 5$

13. An online store charges $10 per cell phone grip and sells 12 million grips per year. For each $0.50 decrease in price, the store sells 1 million more grips. How much should the store charge to maximize yearly revenue? What is the maximum yearly revenue?

14. You drop a water balloon from a height of 50 feet.

    a. Write a function h that gives the height (in feet) of the water balloon above the ground after t seconds. Interpret each term. How long does it take the water balloon to hit the ground?

    b. Find and interpret $h(1) - h(1.5)$.

15. The equation $x^2 - 2kx - 140 = 0$ has the solutions $x = k + 12$ and $x = k - 12$, where k is an integer. Find the possible values of k.

16. The first three figures of a pattern are shown. Is there a figure with 240 tiles in the pattern? If so, which figure is it? If not, explain why not.

Figure 1   Figure 2   Figure 3

Name _____ Date _____

1. Find $\left(2x^3 - 3x^2 + 9x\right) - \left(5x - x^2 + 1\right)$.

In Exercises 2 and 3, write an equation of the parabola in vertex form or intercept form.

2. x-intercepts are -2 and 6; passes through $(4, -9)$

3.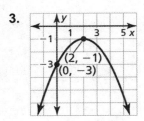

In Exercises 4 and 5, find the product.

4. $(5 - x)(x - 6)$ **5.** $(2x + 9)^2$

In Exercises 6 and 7, solve the equation using any method. Explain your choice of method.

6. $8x^2 - 32 = 0$

7. $5x^2 + 11x - 12 = 0$

8. Write the sentence as an absolute value inequality. Then solve the inequality.

A number is less than 7 units from 2.

9. The table shows the ages of 12 people on a backpacking trip.

Age (years)					
17	16	15	17	20	21
42	18	18	20	18	18

a. Make a box-and-whisker plot that represents the data. Describe the shape of the distribution.

b. Does the data set contain any outliers?

10. Find the minimum or maximum value of $y = -9x^2 - 18x + 7$. Find the domain and range of the function, and when the function is increasing and decreasing.

11. What is the theoretical probability of spinning a multiple of 3 on the spinner?

Use the scale to rate your understanding of the learning target and the success criteria.

| 1 | I do not understand. | 2 | I can do it with help. | 3 | I can do it on my own. | 4 | I can teach someone else. |

	Rating	Date
3.1 Solving Quadratic Equations		
Learning Target: Solve quadratic equations graphically and algebraically.	1 2 3 4	
I can solve quadratic equations by graphing.	1 2 3 4	
I can solve quadratic equations algebraically.	1 2 3 4	
I can use quadratic equations to solve real-life problems.	1 2 3 4	

Name_____ Date_____

3.2 Extra Practice

In Exercises 1–6, find the square root of the number.

1. $\sqrt{-49}$

2. $\sqrt{-16}$

3. $\sqrt{-45}$

4. $6\sqrt{-121}$

5. $-2\sqrt{-100}$

6. $5\sqrt{-75}$

In Exercises 7–12, add, subtract, or multiply. Write the answer in standard form.

7. $(-8 + 3i) + (-1 - 2i)$

8. $(36 - 3i) - (12 + 24i)$

9. $16 + (-16 - 8i) + i$

10. $-5 - (-6 - 6i) -5i$

11. $(-1 + 9i)(15 - i)$

12. $(7 + 2i)^2$

In Exercises 13 and 14, multiply the complex number by its complex conjugate.

13. $13 + i$

14. $-4 - 9i$

15. Find the impedance of the series circuit.

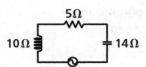

16. $0 = 5x^2 + 25$

17. $x^2 - 10 = -18$

18. $-\frac{1}{3}x^2 = \frac{1}{5} + \frac{4}{3}x^2$

In Exercises 16–18, solve the equation.

In Exercises 19–21, find the zeros of the function.

19. $f(x) = 4x^2 + 24$

20. $g(x) = 12x^2 + 36$

21. $h(x) = 8x^2 + 96$

22. Write a pair of complex numbers whose sum is -10 and whose product is 61.

23. Rewrite each expression with a real denominator.

a. $\dfrac{2 + 7i}{3i}$

b. $\dfrac{4 - 8i}{1 - i}$

24. The sum of two complex numbers is $9 + 7i$. The difference of the numbers is $-3 - 3i$. What is the product of the numbers?

3.2 Review & Refresh

1. Graph $f(x) = -2x + 1$ and its parent function. Then describe the transformation.

2. Simplify $\left(\dfrac{5m^{-4}}{m^{-7}n^0}\right)^2 \cdot \left(\dfrac{-6m^2n^{-1}}{2m^3n^{-4}}\right)^3$. Write your answer using only positive exponents.

3. Find the zeros of the function $f(x) = 5x^2 + 10$. Does the graph of the function intersect the x-axis? Explain your reasoning.

In Exercises 4 and 5, write an equation of a parabola with the given characteristics.

4. focus: $(0, 8)$
   directrix: $y = -8$

5. vertex: $(-3, -1)$
   directrix: $x = -1$

6. A food truck sells sandwiches and salads. Order A includes 2 sandwiches and 1 salad for a total cost of $17.75. Order B includes 6 sandwiches and 4 salads for a total cost of $60. What is the cost of each item?

In Exercises 7 and 8, subtract or multiply. Write your answer in standard form.

7. $(9 + 6i) - (5 - 4i)$ 8. $(1 - 3i)(2 - 8i)$

9. Find the inverse of $f(x) = x^2 - 3, x \le 0$. Then graph the function and its inverse.

10. Graph the system. Identify a solution.
    $2x + y \ge -1$
    $y + 3 < x$

3.2 Self-Assessment

Use the scale to rate your understanding of the learning target and the success criteria.

| 1 | I do not understand. | 2 | I can do it with help. | 3 | I can do it on my own. | 4 | I can teach someone else. |

	Rating	Date
3.2 Complex Numbers		
Learning Target: Understand the imaginary unit i and perform operations with complex numbers.	1 2 3 4	
I can define the imaginary unit i and use it to rewrite the square root of a negative number.	1 2 3 4	
I can add, subtract, and multiply complex numbers.	1 2 3 4	
I can find complex solutions of quadratic equations and complex zeros of quadratic functions.	1 2 3 4	

Name_____ Date _____

3.3 Extra Practice

In Exercises 1–3, solve the equation using square roots.

1. $x^2 + 4x + 4 = 2$

2. $t^2 - 40t + 400 = 300$

3. $9w^2 + 6w + 1 = -18$

In Exercises 4–9, solve the equation by completing the square.

4. $r^2 - 6r - 2 = 0$

5. $x^2 + 10x + 28 = 0$

6. $y(y + 1) = \frac{3}{4}$

7. $2t^2 + 16t - 6 = 0$

8. $3x(2x + 10) = -24$

9. $4x^2 - 5x + 28 = 3x^2 + x$

In Exercises 10–13, decide whether to use factoring, square roots, or completing the square to solve the equation. Explain your reasoning. Then solve the equation.

10. $x^2 + x - 20 = 0$

11. $x^2 + 16x + 64 = -81$

12. $4x^2 + 8x + 12 = 0$

In Exercises 13–15, write the quadratic function in vertex form. Then identify the vertex.

13. $f(x) = x^2 + 6x + 22$

14. $g(x) = x^2 + x - 1$

15. $y = -x^2 + 12x - 31$

16. The height h (in feet) of a golf ball t seconds after it is hit can be modeled by
$h(t) = -16t^2 + 80t + 0.1$.

   a. Find the maximum height of the golf ball.

   b. How long does the ball take to hit the ground?

17. The area of the triangle is 30. Find the value of x.

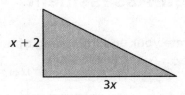

18. You are building a rectangular fence along the side of a lake for an orchard. The river will serve as one side of the fence. You have 80 feet of railing to enclose an area of 782 square feet and want each side of the fence to be at least 18 feet long. What are the dimensions of the fence?

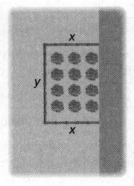

3.3 Review & Refresh

1. Graph $g(x) = 2(x + 3)^2$. Label the vertex, axis of symmetry, and x-intercept(s).

2. Solve $-\dfrac{2s}{3} \leq 12$. Graph the solution.

In Exercises 3 and 4, perform the operation. Write the answer in standard form.

3. $(7 + 3i) + (-4 + i)$ **4.** $(1 - 9i)^2$

5. Identify the function family to which g belongs. Compare the graph of the function to the graph of its parent function.

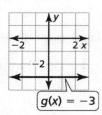

$g(x) = -3$

6. Write $y = x^2 - 12x + 32$ in vertex form. Then identify the vertex.

7. For what value of m are the graphs of $3y = 2x + 9$ and $y = mx - 3$ parallel? perpendicular?

8. Write a function g whose graph is a reflection in the x-axis of the graph of $f(x) = 4|x - 6|$.

9. Write a function that models the data.

x	1	2	3	4	5
y	8	17	34	59	92

10. Solve $3t^2 - 6t + 12 = 0$ by completing the square.

11. A gardener has a rectangular garden. The gardener wants to add 100 square feet to the area of the garden by expanding the existing garden. By what distance x should the length of the garden be expanded?

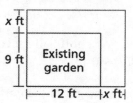

3.3 Self-Assessment

Use the scale to rate your understanding of the learning target and the success criteria.

| 1 | I do not understand. | 2 | I can do it with help. | 3 | I can do it on my own. | 4 | I can teach someone else. |

	Rating	Date
3.3 Completing the Square		
Learning Target: Solve quadratic equations and rewrite quadratic functions by completing the square.	1 2 3 4	
I can solve quadratic equations using square roots.	1 2 3 4	
I can solve quadratic equations by completing the square.	1 2 3 4	
I can apply completing the square to write quadratic functions in vertex form.	1 2 3 4	

3.4 Extra Practice

In Exercises 1–9, solve the equation using the Quadratic Formula. Use technology to check your solution(s).

1. $x^2 - 7x - 18 = 0$

2. $x^2 - 2x + 8 = 0$

3. $3x^2 - 24x + 48 = 0$

4. $x^2 = 4x - 1$

5. $8x = 4x^2 + 5$

6. $5x^2 - 1 = 3x$

7. $-2w^2 - 11 = -6w$

8. $-7z = -4z^2 - 3$

9. $n^2 + 22n = -121$

In Exercises 10–13, find the discriminant of the quadratic equation and describe the number and type of solutions of the equation.

10. $4x^2 - 3x + 11 = 0$

11. $b^2 + 34b + 289 = 0$

12. $x^2 = 3 - 8x$

13. $4q^2 + 1 = 3q$

In Exercises 14–16, find a possible pair of integer values for *a* and *c* so that the quadratic equation has a given number and type of solution(s). Then write the equation.

14. $ax^2 + 12x + c = 0$; one real solution

15. $ax^2 - 5x = c$; two real solutions

16. $2x + c = ax^2$; two imaginary solutions

17. A baseball player hits a foul ball straight up in the air from a height of 4 feet off the ground with an initial velocity of 85 feet per second. Does the ball reach a height of 110 feet? 120 feet? Explain your reasoning.

18. Solve each absolute value equation.

a. $\left| x^2 - 2x - 16 \right| = 1$

b. $x^2 = \left| 6x \right| + 7$

Name _____ Date _____

1. Solve the system using any method. Explain your choice of method.

$$y = -3x + 1$$
$$y = x + 9$$

2. Use the graph to solve $x^2 = x + 2$.

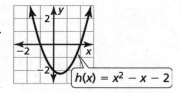

$h(x) = x^2 - x - 2$

3. Solve $x^2 - 2x + 3 = 0$ by completing the square.

4. Find the values of x and y that satisfy the equation $9x - 8i = 27 + yi$.

5. Multiply $-3 + 6i$ by its complex conjugate.

In Exercises 6 and 7, solve the equation by graphing.

6. $-x + 4 = \frac{2}{3}x - 1$ 7. $|x + 3| = |2x + 3|$

In Exercises 8 and 9, solve the equation using the Quadratic Formula.

8. $-5 = 2x^2 + 8x$ 9. $x^2 = 1 - 4x$

10. Write a function g whose graph is a translation 3 units up and 4 units right, followed by a vertical shrink by a factor of $\frac{1}{3}$ of the graph of $f(x) = |x|$.

11. The bar graph shows the results of a survey that asks a group of students their favorite music genre. What percent of the students surveyed chose rock?

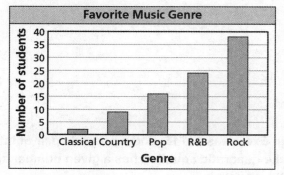

Use the scale to rate your understanding of the learning target and the success criteria.

| 1 | I do not understand. | 2 | I can do it with help. | 3 | I can do it on my own. | 4 | I can teach someone else. |

	Rating	Date
3.4 Using the Quadratic Formula		
Learning Target: Solve and analyze quadratic equations using the Quadratic Formula and discriminants.	1 2 3 4	
I can solve quadratic equations using the Quadratic Formula.	1 2 3 4	
I can find and interpret the discriminant of an equation.	1 2 3 4	
I can write quadratic equations with different numbers of solutions using the discriminant.	1 2 3 4	

Name_____ Date_____

3.5 Extra Practice

In Exercises 1–3, solve the system by graphing.

1. $y = (x - 2)^2$
   $y = \frac{1}{2}x + \frac{1}{2}$

2. $y = -x^2 - 2$
   $y = 4(x + 1) - 3$

3. $y = \frac{1}{2}x^2 - 3$
   $y = -4 - 2x^2$

In Exercises 4–6, solve the system by substitution.

4. $y = x + 4$
   $y = (x + 2)^2 + 1$

5. $x^2 + y^2 = 16$
   $y = -x + 4$

6. $2x^2 + 10x + 48 = y - 10x$
   $-4x^2 - 16x = y$

In Exercises 7–9, solve the system by elimination.

7. $y = 9x^2 + 6x + 2$
   $y = x^2 - 8x - 19$

8. $x^2 - 7x + 11 = y - 1$
   $-x + y = -4$

9. $-5x + 29 = y - x^2$
   $x^2 + y = 2x^2 - 1$

In Exercises 10–13, solve equation by graphing.

10. $x^2 - 3x + 1 = 2x^2 - 5x - 3$

11. $6x^2 + 2x - 3 = -3x^2 + x - 4$

12. $(x - 4)^2 + 3 = (-x + 5)(x - 1) + 12$

13. $(x + 2)(x + 3) - 5 = (x - 1)(x + 2) - 4$

14. The sum of two numbers is -5, and the sum of the squares of the two numbers is 17. What are the two numbers? Explain your reasoning.

15. To be eligible for a free bus pass, a student must live at least 1 mile from the school. For what length of Maple Street are students *not* eligible for a free bus pass?

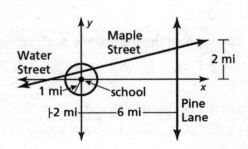

Name _____ Date _____

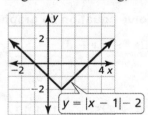

3.5 Review & Refresh

In Exercises 1 and 2, solve the inequality. Graph the solution.

1. $5x - 5 > 10$ **2.** $-2(x + 3) \geq 8$

In Exercises 3 and 4, solve the system using any method. Explain your choice of method.

3. $x^2 + x - 7 = y$ **4.** $x^2 + y^2 = 16$
   $x^2 - 2x - y = 1$ $y = x + 4$

5. Graph $y = \begin{cases} -\frac{3}{2}x + 3, & \text{if } x \leq 2 \\ 2x - 3, & \text{if } x > 2 \end{cases}$. Find the domain and range.

6. A punter kicks a football from an initial height of 3 feet. The ball has an initial velocity of 52 feet per second. Does the football reach a height of 45 feet? Explain your reasoning.

7. For what values of b can you complete the square for $x^2 + bx$ by adding 64?

8. Use technology to find an equation of the line of best fit for the data. Identify and interpret the correlation coefficient.

x	1	4	8	10	16	20
y	3	7	12	17	22	26

9. Find $\sqrt{-48}$.

10. Approximate when the function is positive, negative, increasing, or decreasing.

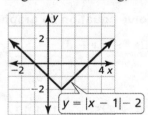

3.5 Self-Assessment

Use the scale to rate your understanding of the learning target and the success criteria.

| 1 | I do not understand. | 2 | I can do it with help. | 3 | I can do it on my own. | 4 | I can teach someone else. |

	Rating	Date
3.5 Solving Nonlinear Systems of Equations		
Learning Target: Solve nonlinear systems graphically and algebraically.	1 2 3 4	
I can describe what a nonlinear system of equations is.	1 2 3 4	
I can solve nonlinear systems using graphing, substitution, or elimination.	1 2 3 4	
I can solve quadratic equations by graphing each side of the equation.	1 2 3 4	

Name_____ Date_____

3.6 Extra Practice

In Exercises 1–4, graph the inequality.

1. $y < x^2 + 2$

2. $y \leq -5x^2$

3. $y \geq -(x + 4)^2 - 1$

4. $y < 4x^2 + 4x + 1$

In Exercises 5–7, graph the system of quadratic inequalities.

5. $y \leq -x^2$
$y > -3x^2 + 3$

6. $y \geq x^2 + 5x$
$y \geq (x + 2)^2 - 1$

7. $y > x^2 - 7x - 8$
$y < -x^2 + 6x + 5$

In Exercises 8–10, solve the inequality algebraically.

8. $16x^2 > 100$

9. $x^2 \leq 15x - 34$

10. $-\frac{1}{5}x^2 + 10x \geq -25$

In Exercises 11–13, solve the inequality by graphing.

11. $x^2 - 6x + 3 \leq -1$

12. $2x^2 - 24 < 8x$

13. $\frac{1}{2}x^2 + 4x \geq 10$

14. A bus is 9 feet tall and 8 feet wide is traveling under an arch. The arch can be modeled by $y = -0.04x^2 + 0.8x + 6$, where x and y are measured in feet.

   a. Will the bus fit under the arch? Explain.

   b. What is the maximum width that a bus 9 feet tall can have and still make it under the arch?

   c. What is the maximum height that a truck 8 feet wide can have and still make it under the arch?

Name _____ Date _____

1. Graph $f(x) = (x + 4)(x - 2)$. Label the x-intercept(s) and the y-intercept.

In Exercises 2 and 3, graph the inequality.

2. $y \geq -2x^2 + 4$ 3. $y < x^2 + 2x - 3$

4. Solve the system of nonlinear equations using the graph.

5. Find the discriminant of $2x^2 - 8x + 4 = 0$ and describe the number and type of solutions of the equation.

6. Solve $3x(x + 8) = -90$ by completing the square.

7. Write an equation for the nth term of the geometric sequence. Then find a_8.

n	1	2	3	4
a_n	12	24	48	96

8. The linear function $m = 700 - 80r$ represents the amount m (in dollars) of money a club has left after booking r hotel rooms.

   a. Interpret the terms and coefficient in the equation.

   b. Find the domain of the function. Is the domain discrete or continuous? Explain.

   c. Graph the function using its domain.

3.6 Self-Assessment

Use the scale to rate your understanding of the learning target and the success criteria.

| 1 | I do not understand. | 2 | I can do it with help. | 3 | I can do it on my own. | 4 | I can teach someone else. |

	Rating	Date
3.6 Quadratic Inequalities		
Learning Target: Graph quadratic inequalities in two variables and solve quadratic inequalities in one variable.	1 2 3 4	
I can describe the graph of a quadratic inequality.	1 2 3 4	
I can graph quadratic inequalities.	1 2 3 4	
I can graph systems of quadratic inequalities.	1 2 3 4	
I can solve quadratic inequalities algebraically and graphically.	1 2 3 4	

Name_____ Date _____

Chapter Self-Assessment

Use the scale to rate your understanding of the learning target and the success criteria.

| 1 | I do not understand. | 2 | I can do it with help. | 3 | I can do it on my own. | 4 | I can teach someone else. |

	Rating	Date
Chapter 3 Quadratic Equations and Complex Numbers		
Learning Target: Understand quadratic equations and complex numbers.	1 2 3 4	
I can perform operations with complex numbers.	1 2 3 4	
I can solve quadratic equations by completing the square.	1 2 3 4	
I can describe how to use the Quadratic Formula.	1 2 3 4	
I can solve nonlinear systems and quadratic inequalities.	1 2 3 4	
3.1 Solving Quadratic Equations		
Learning Target: Solve quadratic equations graphically and algebraically.	1 2 3 4	
I can solve quadratic equations by graphing.	1 2 3 4	
I can solve quadratic equations algebraically.	1 2 3 4	
I can use quadratic equations to solve real-life problems.	1 2 3 4	
3.2 Complex Numbers		
Learning Target: Understand the imaginary unit i and perform operations with complex numbers.	1 2 3 4	
I can define the imaginary unit i and use it to rewrite the square root of a negative number.	1 2 3 4	
I can add, subtract, and multiply complex numbers.	1 2 3 4	
I can find complex solutions of quadratic equations and complex zeros of quadratic functions.	1 2 3 4	
3.3 Completing the Square		
Learning Target: Solve quadratic equations and rewrite quadratic functions by completing the square.	1 2 3 4	
I can solve quadratic equations using square roots.	1 2 3 4	
I can solve quadratic equations by completing the square.	1 2 3 4	
I can apply completing the square to write quadratic functions in vertex form.	1 2 3 4	

Name _____ Date _____

Chapter Self-Assessment (continued)

	Rating	Date
3.4 Using the Quadratic Formula		
Learning Target: Solve and analyze quadratic equations using the Quadratic Formula and discriminants.	1 2 3 4	
I can solve quadratic equations using the Quadratic Formula.	1 2 3 4	
I can find and interpret the discriminant of an equation.	1 2 3 4	
I can write quadratic equations with different numbers of solutions using the discriminant.	1 2 3 4	
3.5 Solving Nonlinear Systems of Equations		
Learning Target: Solve nonlinear systems graphically and algebraically.	1 2 3 4	
I can describe what a nonlinear system of equations is.	1 2 3 4	
I can solve nonlinear systems using graphing, substitution, or elimination.	1 2 3 4	
I can solve quadratic equations by graphing each side of the equation.	1 2 3 4	
3.6 Quadratic Inequalities		
Learning Target: Graph quadratic inequalities in two variables and solve quadratic inequalities in one variable.	1 2 3 4	
I can describe the graph of a quadratic inequality.	1 2 3 4	
I can graph quadratic inequalities.	1 2 3 4	
I can graph systems of quadratic inequalities.	1 2 3 4	
I can solve quadratic inequalities algebraically and graphically.	1 2 3 4	

Name_____ Date_____

1. Which graph represents the inequality $y \geq -x^2 - 4$?

Ⓐ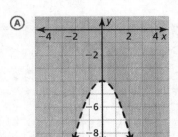

Ⓑ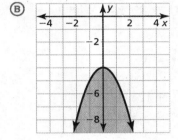

Ⓒ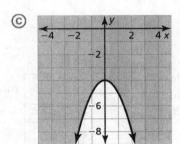

Ⓓ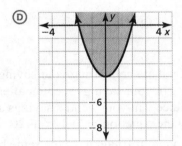

2. The table shows the height of a pumpkin over time after it has been tossed into the air. What type of function can you use to model the data?

Time (seconds), x	0	0.5	1	1.5	2	2.5
Height (feet), y	3	31	51	63	67	63

Ⓐ absolute value

Ⓑ constant

Ⓒ linear

Ⓓ quadratic

3. What are the zeros of the function

$f(x) = 4x^2 + 3x - 10$?

Ⓐ $x = -\frac{5}{2}$ and $x = 1$

Ⓑ $x = -2$ and $x = \frac{5}{4}$

Ⓒ $x = 2$ and $x = -\frac{5}{4}$

Ⓓ $x = \frac{5}{2}$ and $x = -1$

4. What are the solutions to the system?

$x^2 + y^2 = 13$
$-3y = 2x$

Ⓐ $(-2, 3)$ and $(2, -3)$

Ⓑ $(-2, -3)$ and $(2, 3)$

Ⓒ $(-3, 2)$ and $(3, -2)$

Ⓓ $(-3, -2)$ and $(3, 2)$

Chapter 3 **Test Prep** (continued)

5. Let g be a vertical stretch by a factor of 4 and a reflection in the x-axis of the graph of $f(x) = x^2 - 3$. Which is a rule for g?

   Ⓐ $g(x) = -4x^2 + 3$

   Ⓑ $g(x) = -4x^2 + 12$

   Ⓒ $g(x) = -4x^2 - 3$

   Ⓓ $g(x) = -4x^2 - 12$

6. Write an equation of the parabola in standard form.

   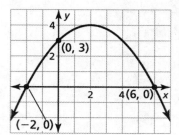

   _____

7. You and your friend are comparing your savings accounts. The table shows the balance in your savings account after different numbers of months. The balance y in your fiend's savings account after x months is represented by the equation $y = 12x + 20$. After how many months do you and your friend have the same balances in your savings accounts?

Your Savings Account	
Month, x	Balance, y
2	60
3	70
4	80
5	90
6	100

8. You and a friend decide to go into business selling bobblehead dolls. The profit p for selling b bobblehead dolls is given by the equation $p(b) = -0.2b^2 + 15b - 150$. How many bobblehead dolls will you have to sell for your profit to be greater than \$100?

   Ⓐ $25 < b < 50$

   Ⓑ $25 \leq b \leq 50$

   Ⓒ $4 < b < 72$

   Ⓓ $0 < b < 25$ *or* $b > 50$

Chapter 3 Test Prep (continued)

9. Which function represents the narrowest parabola?

Ⓐ $y = 2x^2 - 6$

Ⓑ $y = x^2 + 7$

Ⓒ $y = 0.9(x + 5)^2$

Ⓓ $y = -3(x - 4)^2 + 8$

10. A golf ball is hit from the ground, and its height h (in feet) can be modeled by $h(t) = -16t^2 + 128t$, where t is the time (in seconds) after the ball is hit. What is the maximum height of the ball?

feet

11. Select all the expressions that are equivalent to $1 - i$.

Ⓐ $(5 + 6i) + (-4 - 7i)$

Ⓑ $(3 - 9i) - (4 - 8i)$

Ⓒ $i(-1 - i)$

Ⓓ $(1 - i)(1 + i)$

Ⓔ $(5 - 24i) + 4i(5 - 3i) - (16 - 3i)$

Ⓕ $-i^{10} - i^{17}$

12. Which of the given characteristics describe parabolas that open up? Select all that apply.

Ⓐ focus: $(0, -5)$ and directrix: $y = 5$

Ⓑ focus: $(0, 10)$ and directrix: $y = -10$

Ⓒ focus: $(2, 7)$ and directrix: $y = 1$

Ⓓ focus: $(-4, -2)$ and directrix: $y = 4$

Ⓔ focus: $(9, 0)$ and directrix: $x = -9$

Chapter 3

Test Prep (continued)

13. For what value(s) of m does the equation $-6x^2 - 4x + m = 1$ have two real solutions?

- Ⓐ $m < \frac{1}{3}$

- Ⓑ $m = \frac{1}{3}$

- Ⓒ $m \neq \frac{1}{3}$

- Ⓓ $m > \frac{1}{3}$

14. A system of three linear equations in three variables has no solution. Two of the equations are shown below. Which of the following equations could *not* be the third equation in the system?

$$3x + y - z = 8$$
$$-2x - 4y + 5z = 3$$

- Ⓐ $3x + y = 9 + z$

- Ⓑ $5z - 4 = 4y + 2x$

- Ⓒ $3y = 24 + 3z - 9x$

- Ⓓ $-8y + 10z = -7 + 4x$

15. You design a photo editing application. Your revenue (in dollars) for x downloads is given by $f(x) = 5x$ and your profit is $60 less than 85% of the revenue. What is your profit for 300 downloads?

16. The sum of two complex numbers is $9 - 5i$. The difference of the numbers is $(1 - 9i)$. What is the product of the numbers?

_____

Name_____ Date_____

4.1 Extra Practice

In Exercises 1–4, determine whether the function is a polynomial function. If so, write it in standard form and state its degree, type, and leading coefficient.

1. $f(x) = 2x^2 - 3x^4 + 6x + 1$

2. $m(x) = -\frac{3}{7}x^3 + \frac{7}{x} - 3$

3. $g(x) = \sqrt{15}x + \sqrt{5}$

4. $p(x) = -2\sqrt{3} + 3x - 2x^2$

In Exercises 5 and 6, evaluate the function for the given value of x.

5. $h(x) = -x^3 - 2x^2 - 3x + 4;\ x = 2$

6. $g(x) = x^4 - 32x^2 + 256;\ x = -4$

In Exercises 7 and 8, describe the end behavior of the function.

7. $f(x) = -3x^6 + 4x^2 - 3x + 6$

8. $f(x) = \frac{4}{5}x^2 + 6x + 3x^5 - 3x^3 - 2$

In Exercises 9 and 10, graph the polynomial function.

9. $p(x) = 16 - x^4$

10. $g(x) = x^2 + 3x^5 - x$

11. Sketch a graph of the polynomial function f with the following characteristics.

   - f is increasing when $x < -1$ and $0 < x < 1$.

   - f is decreasing when $-1 < x < 0$ and $x > 1$.

   - $f(x) < 0$ for all real numbers.

   Use the graph to describe the degree and leading coefficient of f.

12. A cubic polynomial function g has a leading coefficient of -3 and a constant term of 7. When $g(-2) = 67$ and $g(1) = 13$, what is $g(6)$? Explain your reasoning.

Name _____ Date _____

4.1 Review & Refresh

1. Simplify $m^3(a + 2m) - a(m^3 - 6)$.

2. Write a function g whose graph represents the indicated transformation of the graph of $f(x) = -|x + 2| - 1$.

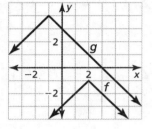

In Exercises 3 and 4, describe the transformation of $f(x) = x^2$ represented by g. Then graph each function.

3. $g(x) = (x - 3)^2$

4. $g(x) = -\frac{4}{3}x^2$

5. Solve the system $y = x^2 - x - 7$ and $y = -2x^2 + 6x - 1$ using any method. Explain your choice of method.

6. You throw a javelin at a track and field meet. The javelin leaves your hand 6 feet above the ground and has an initial velocity of 80 feet per second. Does the javelin reach a height of 100 feet? 110 feet? Explain your reasoning.

7. Solve the inequality $6x + 3 \geq 4x^2$ using any method. Explain your choice of method.

8. Graph $h(x) = 3x^2 - 7 - x - \frac{1}{2}x^3$.

9. Determine whether the function is a polynomial function. If so, write it in standard form and state its degree, type, and leading coefficient.

$$f(x) = \pi x^2 x + \frac{2}{9}x - 7x^4 + x^{-3}x^3 - 9$$

4.1 Self-Assessment

Use the scale to rate your understanding of the learning target and the success criteria.

| 1 | I do not understand. | 2 | I can do it with help. | 3 | I can do it on my own. | 4 | I can teach someone else. |

	Rating	Date
4.1 Graphing Polynomial Functions		
Learning Target: Graph and describe polynomial functions.	1　2　3　4	
I can identify and evaluate polynomial functions.	1　2　3　4	
I can graph polynomial functions.	1　2　3　4	
I can describe end behavior of polynomial functions.	1　2　3　4	

4.2 Extra Practice

In Exercises 1–4, find the sum or difference.

1. $\left(-4x^2 - 6x + 18\right) + \left(-x^2 + 7x + 8\right)$

2. $\left(6x^2 - 12x + 48\right) - \left(-x^2 + 24x - 63\right)$

3. $\left(-11x^4 - x^3 - 3x^2 + 10x - 2\right) - \left(-11x^4 + 5x^2 - 7x + 13\right)$

4. $\left(7x^3 - 9x^5 + 2x - 7 + x^2\right) + \left(-3x^3 + 12 - 5x^2 + 6x^5\right)$

In Exercises 5–12, find the product.

5. $2x^2\left(2x^3 - x^2 + 3x - 5\right)$

6. $\left(x^4 - 10x^2 + 25\right)\left(3x^2 - 6x - 1\right)$

7. $(x + 1)(x - 2)(x + 6)$

8. $(2x - 3)(6 - x)(4 - 5x)$

9. $(3y - 8)(3y + 8)$

10. $(9m + 5)^2$

11. $(2v - 1)^3$

12. $(ab + 7)^3$

In Exercises 13 and 14, use Pascal's Triangle to expand the binomial.

13. $(4t - 2)^4$

14. $(g + 6)^5$

15. A city is planning a new sports park. The total area (in square feet) of the park is modeled by the expression $9x^2 + 4x - 5$. The area of the park designated for soccer fields is modeled by the expression $2x^2 - 5x + 3$. Write an expression that models the area of the park that is not designated for soccer fields.

16. Write an expression for the volume of the cone as a polynomial in standard form.

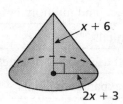

$x + 6$

$2x + 3$

Name _____ Date _____

1. Solve $x^2 + 4x - 1 = -2x^2 + 5x + 4$ by graphing.

In Exercises 2–5, perform the operation.

2. $\left(6x^2 + 7x\right) - \left(9x^2 - 2x + 3\right)$

3. $\left(-5x^3 + x^2 - 8\right) + \left(2x^4 + 3x^3 - 7x + 4\right)$

4. $\left(x^2 + 4x - 8\right)(2x + 3)$

5. $(x + 5)^3$

6. Write an equation of the parabola.

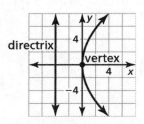

7. Describe the end behavior of the function $f(x) = -4x^7 + 2x^5 + x^2 - 10$.

8. The vertex of a parabola is $(8, -9)$ and one x-intercept is 5. What is the other x-intercept? Explain your reasoning.

9. Graph the system of quadratic inequalities.

$y \le -x^2 - 3x$

$y > x^2 - 4$

10. Evaluate the function $y = 8(4)^x$ when $x = -2$.

In Exercises 11–13, perform the operation. Write the answer in standard form.

11. $(4 + 7i) + (1 - 3i)$

12. $(15 - 8i) - (9 + 2i)$

13. $(5 + i)(9 - i)$

14. You have 23 dollar bills in your wallet. You have $1 bills, $5 bills, and $10 bills. The total value of the 23 dollar bills is $70. There are 5 times as many $1 bills as there are $10 bills. How many of each type of dollar bill do you have?

Use the scale to rate your understanding of the learning target and the success criteria.

| **1** I do not understand. | **2** I can do it with help. | **3** I can do it on my own. | **4** I can teach someone else. |

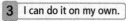

	Rating	Date
4.2 Adding, Subtracting, and Multiplying Polynomials		
Learning Target: Add, subtract, and multiply polynomials.	1 2 3 4	
I can add and subtract polynomials.	1 2 3 4	
I can multiply polynomials and use special product patterns.	1 2 3 4	
I can use Pascal's Triangle to expand binomials.	1 2 3 4	

Name_____ Date _____

4.3 Extra Practice

In Exercises 1–4, divide using long division.

1. $\left(x^2 + 6x + 12\right) \div (x - 3)$

2. $\left(x^3 - 4x^2\right) \div \left(x^2 - 16\right)$

3. $\left(4x^3 + 13x^2 + 27x + 6\right) \div (4x + 1)$

4. $\left(x^4 + 2x^3 + 5x^2 + 3x\right) \div \left(x^2 - x\right)$

In Exercises 5–8, divide using synthetic division.

5. $\left(x^2 - 10x + 2\right) \div (x - 2)$

6. $\left(x^3 + 4x^2 + 6x + 4\right) \div (x + 2)$

7. $\left(2x^3 - 54\right) \div (x + 3)$

8. $\left(2x^4 - 11x^3 + 11x^2 + 4x + 4\right) \div (x - 4)$

In Exercises 9–12, match the equivalent expressions. Justify your answers.

9. $\left(x^2 - x - 8\right) \div (x - 4)$

A. $x + 3 + \dfrac{4}{x - 4}$

10. $\left(x^2 - x + 8\right) \div (x - 4)$

B. $x + 5 + \dfrac{12}{x - 4}$

11. $\left(x^2 + x - 8\right) \div (x - 4)$

C. $x + 5 + \dfrac{28}{x - 4}$

12. $\left(x^2 + x + 8\right) \div (x - 4)$

D. $x + 3 + \dfrac{20}{x - 4}$

In Exercises 13–16, use synthetic division to evaluate the function for the indicated value of x.

13. $f(x) = -3x^3 + 4x^2 - 17x - 6; x = 2$

14. $f(x) = -x^4 + x^2 + 4; x = -1$

15. $f(x) = x^3 - 10x^2 + 31x - 30; x = -5$

16. $f(x) = x^3 + 8x + 27; x = 3$

17. What is the value of k such that $\left(-x^4 + 5x^2 + kx - 8\right) \div (x - 4)$ has a remainder of 0?

Name _____ Date _____

4.3 Review & Refresh

In Exercises 1 and 2, find the zero(s) of the function.

1. $f(x) = x^2 - 14x + 49$

2. $h(x) = 4x^2 + 100$

3. Use synthetic division to evaluate
   $f(x) = 2x^3 - x^2 + 5$ when $x = -2$.

4. Write an equation of the parabola in vertex form.

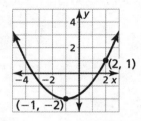

(2, 1)
(−1, −2)

5. For what value of k is the expression
   $(x + 4)(kx^2 - 5x - 4) - (3x^3 + 7x^2 - 4x)$
   equal to $-x^3 - 4x^2 - 20x - 16$?

6. Graph $f(x) = x^3 + 4x^2 + x - 6$.

7. Divide $2x^4 - 6x^2 + 3x + 1$ by $x^2 + x - 3$.

In Exercises 8 and 9, solve the equation.

8. $8^{3x} = 8^{2x+9}$

9. $3^{x+8} = 81$

10. The table shows the results of rolling a 6-sided number cube 20 times. What is the experimental probability of rolling a 5?

1	2	3	4	5	6
3	4	1	3	5	4

In Exercises 11–13, simplify the expression.

11. $\sqrt{40x^5}$

12. $\sqrt{\dfrac{5}{64}}$

13. $4\sqrt{3} - \sqrt{108}$

14. City officials want to build a rectangular skate park. The skate park must have a perimeter of 200 yards and an area of at least 900 square yards. Describe the possible lengths of the skate park.

4.3 Self-Assessment

Use the scale to rate your understanding of the learning target and the success criteria.

| 1 | I do not understand. | 2 | I can do it with help. | 3 | I can do it on my own. | 4 | I can teach someone else. |

	Rating	Date
4.3 Dividing Polynomials		
Learning Target: Divide polynomials by other polynomials and use the Remainder Theorem.	1 2 3 4	
I can use long division to divide polynomials by other polynomials.	1 2 3 4	
I can divide polynomials by binomials of the form $x - k$ using synthetic division.	1 2 3 4	
I can explain the Remainder Theorem.	1 2 3 4	

4.4 Extra Practice

In Exercises 1–14, factor the polynomial completely.

1. $20x^3 - 220x^2 + 600x$

2. $m^5 - 81m$

3. $27a^3 + 8b^3$

4. $5t^6 + 2t^5 - 5t^4 - 2t^3$

5. $y^4 - 13y^2 - 48$

6. $5p^3 + 5p - 5p^2 - 5$

7. $810k^4 - 160$

8. $a^5 + a^3 - a^2 - 1$

9. $2x^6 - 8x^5 - 42x^4$

10. $5z^3 + 5z^2 - 6z - 6$

11. $12x^2 - 22x - 20$

12. $3m^2 - 48m^6$

13. $4x^3 - 4x^2 + x$

14. $5m^4 - 70m^3 + 245m^2$

In Exercises 15–17, show that the binomial is a factor of the polynomial. Then factor the polynomial completely.

15. $f(x) = x^3 - 13x - 12; \ x + 1$

16. $f(x) = 6x^3 + 8x^2 - 34x - 12; \ x - 2$

17. $f(x) = 2x^4 - 12x^3 + 6x^2 + 20x; \ x - 5$

18. Factor each polynomial completely.

    a. $5a^2c - 3a^2d - 5b^2c + 3b^2d$

    b. $x^{2n} + 6x^n + 9$

19. What is the value of k such that $x - 6$ is a factor of $f(x) = 3x^3 - 17x^2 - kx + 18$? Justify your answer.

Name _____ Date _____

4.4 Review & Refresh

In Exercises 1–4, solve the equation using any method. Explain your choice of method.

1. $x^2 + 10x - 11 = 0$ **2.** $4x^2 - 29x + 7 = 0$

3. $x^2 + 6x = 17$ **4.** $2x^2 - 3x - 1 = 0$

5. Divide $-x^3 - x^2 + 17x - 15$ by $x + 5$.

6. Write an expression for the area and perimeter of the figure shown.

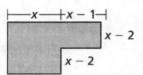

In Exercises 7 and 8, factor the polynomial completely.

7. $z^3 - 4z^2 - 9z + 36$

8. $81b^4 - 25$

9. Determine whether the table represents an *exponential growth function*, an *exponential decay function*, or *neither*. Explain.

x	–1	0	1	2
y	8	12	18	27

10. Graph $f(x) = -(x + 3)^2 - 1$. Label the vertex and axis of symmetry.

11. Determine whether the data show a linear relationship. If so, write an equation of a line of fit. Then estimate y when $x = 24$ and explain its meaning in the context of the situation.

Time (months), x	3	6	9	12	15
Savings (dollars), y	133	178	223	268	313

4.4 Self-Assessment

Use the scale to rate your understanding of the learning target and the success criteria.

1 I do not understand.	**2** I can do it with help.	**3** I can do it on my own.	**4** I can teach someone else.

	Rating	Date
4.4 Factoring Polynomials		
Learning Target: Factor polynomials and use the Factor Theorem.	1 2 3 4	
I can find common monomial factors of polynomials.	1 2 3 4	
I can factor polynomials.	1 2 3 4	
I can use the Factor Theorem.	1 2 3 4	

54 **Algebra 2**
Practice Workbook and Test Prep

4.5 Extra Practice

In Exercises 1–6, solve the equation.

1. $36r^3 - r = 0$

2. $20x^3 + 80x^2 = -60x$

3. $3m^2 = 75m^4$

4. $-13y^2 + 36 = -y^4$

5. $2x^3 - x^2 - 2x = -1$

6. $-20c^2 + 50c = 8c^3 - 125$

In Exercises 7–10, find the zeros of the function. Then sketch a graph of the function.

7. $f(x) = x^4 - x^3 - 12x^2$

8. $f(x) = -4x^3 + 12x^2 - 9x$

9. $f(x) = x^3 + 4x^2 - 6x - 24$

10. $f(x) = x^4 - 18x^2 + 81$

11. Find all the real solutions of $x^3 - 8x^2 - 21x + 108 = 0$.

12. Find all the real zeros of $f(x) = 3x^4 + 11x^3 - 40x^2 - 132x + 48$.

13. Write a polynomial function g of least degree that has rational coefficients, a leading coefficient of 1, and the zeros -5 and $4 + \sqrt{2}$.

14. All the possible rational solutions and actual rational solutions of the equation below are shown. Complete the equation.

    Possible: $\pm 1,\ \pm 2,\ \pm 3,\ \pm 6,\ \pm \frac{1}{2},\ \pm \frac{3}{2}$

    Actual: $-3,\ \frac{1}{2}$

    $(x + \underline{\quad})(x + \underline{\quad})(x^2 + \underline{\quad}) = 0$

Name _____ Date _____

In Exercises 1–5, find the product or quotient.

1. $(3b + 4)(3b - 4)$ 2. $(6x + 1)^2$

3. $(8p - 2)^3$ 4. $(mn + 9)^3$

5. $(x^4 - 9x^3 + 18x^2 - 17x + 18) \div (x - 2)$

6. Identify the function family to which f belongs. Describe the transformation from the graph of the parent function to the graph of f.

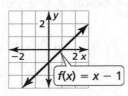

7. Write a function to model the data.

x	–3	–2	–1	0	1
y	34	20	10	4	2

8. Write the function $f(x) = x^2 + 5x + 7$ in vertex form. Then identify the vertex.

In Exercises 9 and 10, find all the real zeros of the function.

9. $f(x) = x^3 + 2x^2 - 33x - 90$

10. $g(x) = 72x^3 - 345x^2 + 434x - 49$

In Exercises 11–14, solve the equation.

11. $3x^2 - 6 = 0$ 12. $9x^2 + 81 = 0$

13. $-4 = 2x^2 + 6$ 14. $4 = \frac{1}{2}(x - 5)^2 - 3$

15. The profit P (in millions of dollars) for a manufacturer of wireless headphones can be modeled by $P = -\frac{1}{6}(x^3 - 52x)$, where x is the number (in millions) of wireless headphones produced. Currently, the company produces 6 million headphones and makes a profit of $16 million. What lesser number of headphones could the company produce and still make the same profit?

Use the scale to rate your understanding of the learning target and the success criteria.

| 1 | I do not understand. | 2 | I can do it with help. | 3 | I can do it on my own. | 4 | I can teach someone else. |

4.5 Solving Polynomial Equations	Rating	Date
Learning Target: Solve polynomial equations and find zeros of polynomial functions.	1 2 3 4	
I can explain how solutions of equations and zeros of functions are related.	1 2 3 4	
I can solve polynomial equations.	1 2 3 4	
I can write a polynomial function when given information about its zeros.	1 2 3 4	

Name_____ Date_____

4.6 Extra Practice

In Exercises 1 and 2, identify the number of solutions of the polynomial equation. Then find all the solutions.

1. $2x^3 - 11x^2 - 2x + 2 = 0$

2. $x^4 + x^3 + 3x^2 + 9x = 54$

In Exercises 3–6, find all the zeros of the polynomial function.

3. $h(x) = x^4 - 3x^3 + 6x^2 + 2x - 60$

4. $f(x) = x^3 - 3x^2 - 15x + 125$

5. $g(x) = x^4 - 48x^2 - 49$

6. $h(x) = -5x^3 + 9x^2 - 18x - 4$

In Exercises 7 and 8, determine the number of imaginary zeros for the function with the given degree and graph. Explain your reasoning.

7. Degree: 3

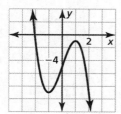

8. Degree: 4

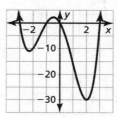

In Exercises 9–12, write a polynomial function f of least degree that has rational coefficients, a leading coefficient of 1, and the given zeros.

9. $-4, 1, 7$

10. $10, -\sqrt{5}$

11. $8, 3, -i$

12. $0, 2 - \sqrt{2}, 2 + 3i$

In Exercises 13 and 14, determine the possible numbers of positive real zeros, negative real zeros, and imaginary zeros for the function.

13. $g(x) = x^5 - 3x^4 - 7x^2 + 9$

14. $g(x) = x^6 + 2x^5 + x^4 - 3x^3 - 5x^2 + x - 8$

15. Three zeros of $f(x) = x^4 - x^3 - 4x^2 - 16x - 320$ are 5, $4i$, and $-4i$. Is the fourth zero *real* or *imaginary*? Explain your reasoning.

Name _____ Date _____

In Exercises 1–4, match the function with the correct graph. Explain your reasoning.

1. $f(x) = x(x + 2)(x - 1)$

2. $g(x) = (x - 3)(x - 1)(x + 2)$

3. $h(x) = x(x - 2)(x + 1)$

4. $k(x) = (x + 3)(x + 1)(x - 2)$

A.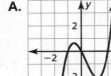

B.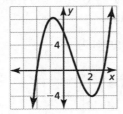

C.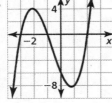

D.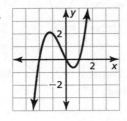

5. Solution A is 65% chloride and Solution B is 80% chloride. How much of each solution should a chemist mix to make 5 cups of a solution that is 75% chloride?

6. Write a function g whose graph represents a reflection in the x-axis, followed by a translation 5 units left and 9 units down of the graph of $f(x) = x^2$.

In Exercises 7 and 8, determine the possible numbers of positive real zeros, negative real zeros, and imaginary zeros for the function. Then find the zeros.

7. $f(x) = 3x^3 + 2x^2 - 7x + 2$

8. $g(x) = x^4 + 3x^3 - 6x^2 + 12x - 40$

4.6 Self-Assessment

Use the scale to rate your understanding of the learning target and the success criteria.

| 1 I do not understand. | 2 I can do it with help. | 3 I can do it on my own. | 4 I can teach someone else. |

	Rating	Date
4.6 The Fundamental Theorem of Algebra		
Learning Target: Use the Fundamental Theorem of Algebra to find all complex roots of polynomial equations.	1 2 3 4	
I can identify the degree of a polynomial.	1 2 3 4	
I can explain the Fundamental Theorem of Algebra.	1 2 3 4	
I can find all the zeros of a polynomial function.	1 2 3 4	

Name_____ Date_____

4.7 Extra Practice

In Exercises 1–4, describe the transformation of *f* represented by *g*. Then graph each function.

1. $f(x) = x^4$; $g(x) = x^4 - 9$

2. $f(x) = x^5$; $g(x) = (x + 1)^5 + 2$

3. $f(x) = x^6$; $g(x) = -5(x - 2)^6$

4. $f(x) = x^3$; $g(x) = \left(\frac{1}{2}x\right)^3 - 4$

In Exercises 5 and 6, write a rule for *g* and then graph each function. Describe the graph of *g* as a transformation of the graph of *f*.

5. $f(x) = x^3 + 8$; $g(x) = f(-x) - 9$

6. $f(x) = 2x^5 - x^3 + 1$; $g(x) = 5f(x)$

In Exercises 7 and 8, write a rule for *g* that represents the indicated transformation of the graph of *f*.

7. $f(x) = x^3 - 6x^2 + 5$; translation 1 unit left, followed by a reflection in the *x*-axis and a vertical stretch by a factor of 2

8. $f(x) = 3x^4 + x^3 + 3x^2 + 12$; horizontal shrink by a factor of $\frac{1}{3}$ and a translation 8 units down, followed by a reflection in the *y*-axis.

9. Write a function *V* for the volume (in cubic centimeters) of the cylinder shown. Then write a function *W* that represents the volume (in cubic centimeters) of the cylinder when *x* is measured in millimeters. Find and interpret $W(2)$.

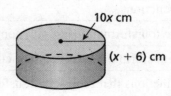

10x cm

(x + 6) cm

Name _____ Date _____

1. Find the minimum or maximum value of the function $f(x) = -x^2 - 2x + 15$. Find the domain and range of the function, and when the function is increasing and decreasing.

2. Find all the zeros of
$f(x) = 5x^3 - 26x^2 - 9x + 12$.

3. The volume (in cubic inches) of a gift box in the shape of a rectangular prism can be modeled by $V = 2x^3 - 29x^2 + 137x - 210$, where x is the length (in inches). Determine the values of x for which the model makes sense. Explain.

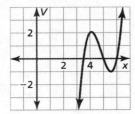

4. Write an equation in intercept form of the parabola that passes through $(-9, 45)$ and has x-intercepts -10 and 6.

5. How many solutions does $x^4 - 3x^2 - 4 = 0$ have? Find all the solutions.

In Exercises 6 and 7, perform the operation. Write your answer in standard form.

6. $(8 + 5i) - (-4 + 9i)$

7. $(2 + 12i)(-4 + 6i)$

8. Write an inequality that is represented by the graph.

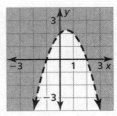

9. Let $f(x) = x^4 - 4x^2 - 1$ and $g(x) = \frac{1}{2} f(x)$. Write a rule for g and then graph each function. Describe the graph of g as a transformation of the graph of f.

Use the scale to rate your understanding of the learning target and the success criteria.

| 1 | I do not understand. | 2 | I can do it with help. | 3 | I can do it on my own. | 4 | I can teach someone else. |

	Rating	Date
4.7 Transformations of Polynomial Functions		
Learning Target: Describe and graph transformations of polynomial functions.	1 2 3 4	
I can describe transformations of polynomial functions.	1 2 3 4	
I can graph transformations of polynomial functions.	1 2 3 4	
I can write functions that represent transformations of polynomial functions.	1 2 3 4	

4.8 Extra Practice

In Exercises 1 and 2, graph the function.

1. $h(x) = -\frac{1}{3}(x + 1)(x - 2)^2$

2. $k(x) = (x + 3)(x^2 - 2x + 2)$

In Exercises 3 and 4, find all the real zeros of the function.

3. $f(x) = 2x^3 + 11x^2 + 2x - 15$

4. $p(x) = 6x^4 + 34x^3 - 45x^2 + 74x - 21$

In Exercises 5–8, graph the function. Identify the _x_-intercepts and the points where the local maximums and local minimums occur. Determine the interval for which the function is increasing or decreasing.

5. $f(x) = 4x^3 - 12x^2 - x + 15$

6. $g(x) = 2x^4 + 5x^3 - 21x^2 - 10x$

7. $k(x) = x^3 - 2x$

8. $f(x) = x^4 - 29x^2 + 100$

9. Write and graph a polynomial function that has one real zero in each of the intervals $-4 < x < -3, -1 < x < 0$, and $2 < x < 3$. Is there a maximum degree that such a polynomial function can have? Justify your answer.

Name_____ Date _____

4.8 Review & Refresh

1. Determine whether the data are *linear*, *quadratic*, or *neither*. Explain.

Time (days), x	0	1	2	3
Price (dollars), y	12	15.2	18.5	21.9

2. A soccer goalie punts a soccer ball. The height h (in feet) of the ball t seconds after it is punted can be modeled by $h = -16t^2 + 36t + 2$.

   a. Find the maximum height of the ball.

   b. A soccer player kicks the ball when it is 2 feet above the ground. How long is the ball in the air?

3. Describe the transformation of $f(x) = x^3$ represented by $g(x) = (x - 3)^3 + 2$. Then graph each function.

4. Divide $\left(3x^2 - 11x - 8\right)$ by $(x - 5)$.

5. Find all the zeros of
   $f(x) = x^5 + 4x^4 + x^3 - 2x^2 - 12x - 72$.

6. Use the graph to solve $2x^2 + 4 = -6x$.

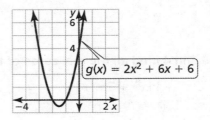

7. Graph $f(x) = x^4 + 2x^3 - 5x^2 - 6x$. Identify the x-intercepts and the points where the local maximums and local minimums occur, Determine the intervals for which the function is increasing or decreasing.

8. Find $(5z + 7)(5z - 7)$.

4.8 Self-Assessment

Use the scale to rate your understanding of the learning target and the success criteria.

1	I do not understand.	2	I can do it with help.	3	I can do it on my own.	4	I can teach someone else.

	Rating	Date
4.8 Analyzing Graphs of Polynomial Functions		
Learning Target: Analyze graphs of polynomial functions.	1 2 3 4	
I can identify a turning point of a polynomial function.	1 2 3 4	
I can analyze real zeros and turning points numerically.	1 2 3 4	
I can explain the relationship among the degree of a polynomial function, real zeros, and turning points.	1 2 3 4	

4.9 Extra Practice

In Exercises 1–4, write a cubic function whose graph passes through the given points.

1.
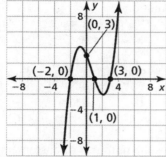

2.
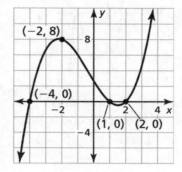

3. $(-6, 0), (-5, 0), (4, 0), (5, 110)$

4. $(-1, 0), (0, 36), (3, 0), (6, 0)$

In Exercises 5–8, use finite differences to determine the degree of the polynomial function that fits the data. Then use technology to find the polynomial function.

5.

x	−2	−1	0	1	2	3
f(x)	−14	−6.5	0	5.5	10	13.5

6.

x	−2	−1	0	1	2
f(x)	30	4	0	0	−14

7. $(0, 0), (2, 0), (4, 40), (6, 168), (8, 432), (10, 880)$

8. $(0, 10), (1, 10), (2, 18), (3, 64), (4, 202), (5, 510)$

9. The table shows the population y (in thousands) of bacteria after x hours. Find a model for the data. Use the model to estimate the population of the bacteria after 2 hours.

x	0.5	1	2.5	3	4	4.5
y	5.125	6	20.625	32	69	96.125

10. The table shows the value y (in hundreds of dollars) of an autographed jersey of a professional football player, where x represents the number of years since 2010. Find a model for the data. Use the model to estimate the year that the jersey will be valued at $500,000.

x	1	2	3	4	5
y	6	34	162	510	1246

4.9 Review & Refresh

1. Use the graph to describe the degree and leading coefficient of f.

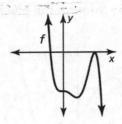

5. Determine the possible numbers of positive real zeros, negative real zeros, and imaginary zeros for the function
$$g(x) = x^5 - 5x^4 + 10x^2 + 5x + 1.$$

2. Let the graph of g be a translation 4 units right and 7 units up, followed by a reflection in the x-axis of the graph of $f(x) = (x - 3)^3 - 5$. Write a rule for g.

3. Solve the system using any method. Explain your choice of method.
$$x^2 - 4x - y = 0$$
$$2x^2 + x + y = 6$$

6. The table shows the numbers of customers y in a line at a grocery store x minutes after noon. Use technology to find an equation of the line of best fit. Interpret the slope and y-intercept in this situation.

x	0	1	2	3	4	5	6
y	16	15	13	11	10	9	5

4. Write a cubic function whose graph is shown.

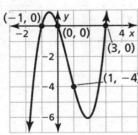
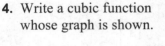

7. Solve $x^2 - 6x = -x^2 + 4$.

8. Write an expression for the volume of the rectangular prism as a polynomial in standard form.

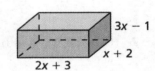

4.9 Self-Assessment

Use the scale to rate your understanding of the learning target and the success criteria.

1	I do not understand.	2	I can do it with help.	3	I can do it on my own.	4	I can teach someone else.

	Rating	Date
4.9 Modeling with Polynomial Functions		
Learning Target: Write polynomial functions.	1 2 3 4	
I can write a polynomial function given a graph or set of points.	1 2 3 4	
I can write a polynomial function using finite differences.	1 2 3 4	
I can use technology to find a polynomial model for a set of data.	1 2 3 4	

Name_____ Date_____

Use the scale to rate your understanding of the learning target and the success criteria.

1 I do not understand.	**2** I can do it with help.	**3** I can do it on my own.	**4** I can teach someone else.

	Rating	Date
Chapter 4 Polynomial Functions		
Learning Target: Understand polynomial functions.	1 2 3 4	
I can graph polynomial functions.	1 2 3 4	
I can add, subtract, multiply, divide, and factor polynomial functions.	1 2 3 4	
I can solve polynomial equations.	1 2 3 4	
I can model with and analyze graphs of polynomial functions.	1 2 3 4	
4.1 Graphing Polynomial Functions		
Learning Target: Graph and describe polynomial functions.	1 2 3 4	
I can identify and evaluate polynomial functions.	1 2 3 4	
I can graph polynomial functions.	1 2 3 4	
I can describe end behavior of polynomial functions.	1 2 3 4	
4.2 Adding, Subtracting, and Multiplying Polynomials		
Learning Target: Add, subtract, and multiply polynomials.	1 2 3 4	
I can add and subtract polynomials.	1 2 3 4	
I can multiply polynomials and use special product patterns.	1 2 3 4	
I can use Pascal's Triangle to expand binomials.	1 2 3 4	
4.3 Dividing Polynomials		
Learning Target: Divide polynomials by other polynomials and use the Remainder Theorem.	1 2 3 4	
I can use long division to divide polynomials by other polynomials.	1 2 3 4	
I can divide polynomials by binomials of the form $x - k$ using synthetic division.	1 2 3 4	
I can explain the Remainder Theorem.	1 2 3 4	
4.4 Factoring Polynomials		
Learning Target: Factor polynomials and use the Factor Theorem.	1 2 3 4	
I can find common monomial factors of polynomials.	1 2 3 4	
I can factor polynomials.	1 2 3 4	
I can use the Factor Theorem.	1 2 3 4	

Chapter 4

Chapter Self-Assessment (continued)

	Rating	Date
4.5 Solving Polynomial Equations		
Learning Target: Solve polynomial equations and find zeros of polynomial functions.	1 2 3 4	
I can explain how solutions of equations and zeros of functions are related.	1 2 3 4	
I can solve polynomial equations.	1 2 3 4	
I can write a polynomial function when given information about its zeros.	1 2 3 4	
4.6 The Fundamental Theorem of Algebra		
Learning Target: Use the Fundamental Theorem of Algebra to find all complex roots of polynomial equations.	1 2 3 4	
I can identify the degree of a polynomial.	1 2 3 4	
I can explain the Fundamental Theorem of Algebra.	1 2 3 4	
I can find all the zeros of a polynomial function.	1 2 3 4	
4.7 Transformations of Polynomial Functions		
Learning Target: Describe and graph transformations of polynomial functions.	1 2 3 4	
I can describe transformations of polynomial functions.	1 2 3 4	
I can graph transformations of polynomial functions.	1 2 3 4	
I can write functions that represent transformations of polynomial functions.	1 2 3 4	
4.8 Analyzing Graphs of Polynomial Functions		
Learning Target: Analyze graphs of polynomial functions.	1 2 3 4	
I can identify a turning point of a polynomial function.	1 2 3 4	
I can analyze real zeros and turning points numerically.	1 2 3 4	
I can explain the relationship among the degree of a polynomial function, real zeros, and turning points.	1 2 3 4	
4.9 Modeling with Polynomial Functions		
Learning Target: Write polynomial functions.	1 2 3 4	
I can write a polynomial function given a graph or set of points.	1 2 3 4	
I can write a polynomial function using finite differences.	1 2 3 4	
I can use technology to find a polynomial model for a set of data.	1 2 3 4	

Chapter 4 Test Prep

1. The function $d(t) = 65t$ represents the distance (in miles) of a car t hours after it merges onto a highway. Which function family does d belong to?

Ⓐ constant

Ⓑ linear

Ⓒ absolute value

Ⓓ quadratic

2. Which statement about the graph of function g is true?

Ⓐ The degree of g is even and the leading coefficient of g is positive.

Ⓑ The degree of g is odd and the leading coefficient of g is positive.

Ⓒ The degree of g is even and the leading coefficient of g is negative.

Ⓓ The degree of g is odd and the leading coefficient of g is negative.

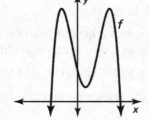

3. What is the directrix of $y = -\frac{1}{32}(x + 6)^2 - 1$?

Ⓐ $y = -9$

Ⓑ $y = 2$

Ⓒ $y = 7$

Ⓓ $y = 14$

4. Which cubic function represents the graph shown?

Ⓐ $f(x) = \frac{1}{3}(x + 1)(x - 2)(x - 4)$

Ⓑ $f(x) = (x + 1)(x - 2)(x - 4)$

Ⓒ $f(x) = \frac{1}{3}(x - 1)(x + 2)(x + 4)$

Ⓓ $f(x) = (x - 1)(x + 2)(x + 4)$

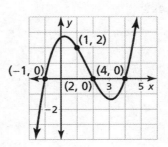

Chapter 4 **Test Prep** (continued)

5. Which statement about the function f is false?

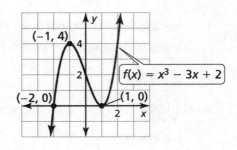

Ⓐ −2 and 1 are zeros of the function.

Ⓑ The function has a local minimum at $x = 1$ and a local maximum at $x = -1$.

Ⓒ The function is increasing when $x < -1$ and $x > 1$, and decreasing when $-1 < x < 1$.

Ⓓ The function is odd.

6. Let the graph of g be a translation 3 units down, followed by a horizontal shrink by a factor of $\frac{1}{2}$ of the graph of $f(x) = |x|$. Which of the following is a rule for g?

Ⓐ $g(x) = 2|x| - 6$

Ⓑ $g(x) = |2x| - 3$

Ⓒ $g(x) = \frac{1}{2}|x| - \frac{3}{2}$

Ⓓ $g(x) = \left|\frac{1}{2}x\right| - 3$

7. Write a polynomial function f of least degree that has rational coefficients, a leading coefficient of 1, and the zeros 3, −2, and 2i.

8. A civil engineer plans to construct a cable suspension bridge in your town. The cable being used will form a curve modeled by the equation $h(x) = 3x^2 - 6x + 200$, where x represents the length of cable used (in feet) and $h(x)$ represents the height of the cable (in feet). At what height will the cable hang closest to the bridge deck?

feet

⊖	⊖	⊖	⊖	⊖	⊖
	⊘	⊘	⊘	⊘	
⊙	⊙	⊙	⊙	⊙	⊙
⓪	⓪	⓪	⓪	⓪	⓪
①	①	①	①	①	①
②	②	②	②	②	②
③	③	③	③	③	③
④	④	④	④	④	④
⑤	⑤	⑤	⑤	⑤	⑤
⑥	⑥	⑥	⑥	⑥	⑥
⑦	⑦	⑦	⑦	⑦	⑦
⑧	⑧	⑧	⑧	⑧	⑧
⑨	⑨	⑨	⑨	⑨	⑨

Chapter 4

Test Prep (continued)

9. Which is *not* a possible classification of the zeros for
   $f(x) = x^4 - 5x^3 + 6x + 1?$

   Ⓐ no positive real zeros, no negative real zeros, four imaginary zeros

   Ⓑ no positive real zeros, four negative real zeros, no imaginary zeros

   Ⓒ two positive real zeros, no negative real zeros, two imaginary zeros

   Ⓓ two positive real zeros, two negative real zeros, no imaginary zeros

10. A spectator in a stadium drops their sunglasses from a height of 75 feet. How long does it take the sunglasses to hit the ground? Round your answer to the nearest hundredth of a second.

    seconds

11. Consider the function

    $f(x) = x^3 - 2x^2 - 19x + 20.$

    For what values of k does $\dfrac{f(x)}{x - k}$ have a remainder *not* equal to 0? Select all that apply.

    Ⓐ 10

    Ⓑ 5

    Ⓒ 4

    Ⓓ −1

    Ⓔ −2

    Ⓕ −4

12. During a recent period of time, the numbers (in millions) of new football F and new baseball B jersey sales can be modeled

    $F = 12t^4 - 20t^3 - 20t + 900$

    $B = 15t^4 - 10t^3 + 10t^2 - 30t + 700$

    where t represents the time in years. Write a polynomial J to model the total number of new football and baseball jersey sales.

Chapter 4 **Test Prep** (continued)

13. The function $V(x) = 27x^2 - 9x$ represents the volume (in cubic yards) of the cylinder. The function $W(x) = V\left(\frac{1}{3}x\right)$ represents the volume (in cubic yards) of the cylinder when x is measured in feet. Find $W(15)$.

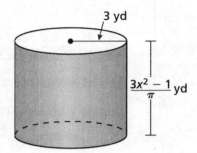

3 yd

$\dfrac{3x^2 - 1}{\pi}$ yd

cubic yards

14. A landscaper is designing a flower garden in the shape of a trapezoid. She wants the shorter base to be 3 yards greater than the height and the longer base to be 7 yards greater than the height. The total area of the flower garden is 150 square yards. What will the length of the longer base?

yards

15. What is the value of k such that $\left(3x^3 - 6x^2 + kx - 12\right) \div (x - 3)$ has a remainder of 0?

Ⓐ -41

Ⓑ -5

Ⓒ 4

Ⓓ 5

16. Select all the expressions that have an answer that is a pure imaginary number.

Ⓐ $(3 - 7i) - 2(1 + 5i) - 1$

Ⓑ $(5 - 2i)(4 + i) - (20 - 6i)$

Ⓒ $\left(-6 + i^6\right) + 8i^3 + 7$

Ⓓ $\left(9 + 3i^5\right) + i\left(7 - 2i^2\right) - 2(-4 + 7i)$

Name_____ Date_____

5.1 Extra Practice

In Exercises 1–3, find the indicated real *n*th root(s) of *a*.

1. $n = 3$, $a = -343$ 2. $n = 2$, $a = -400$ 3. $n = 6$, $a = 64$

In Exercises 4–11, evaluate the expression without using technology.

4. $64^{1/2}$ 5. $625^{1/4}$ 6. $32^{7/5}$ 7. $16^{3/4}$

8. $(-27)^{1/3}$ 9. $(-32)^{3/5}$ 10. $49^{-3/2}$ 11. $1000^{-2/3}$

In Exercises 12–15, evaluate the expression using technology. Round your answer to two decimal places, if necessary.

12. $\sqrt[5]{15{,}013}$ 13. $3975^{1/7}$ 14. $(-18)^{-3/5}$ 15. $\left(\sqrt[6]{3}\right)^{5}$

In Exercises 16–21, find the real solution(s) of the equation. Round your answer to two decimal places, if necessary.

16. $6x^3 = -6$ 17. $(x - 9)^2 = 10$

18. $2(x + 5)^4 = 128$ 19. $x^5 - 32 = -64$

20. $-\frac{1}{4}x^5 = 256$ 21. $-\frac{1}{10}x^3 + 100 = 0$

22. Between which two consecutive integers does $\sqrt[5]{2000}$ lie? Explain your reasoning.

23. The volume of a cube is 1728 cubic inches. What is the side length of the cube?

24. A cone has a height of 6 meters, a radius of *r* meters, and a volume of 57 cubic meters. What is the radius of the cone?

5.1   Review & Refresh

1. Graph $g(x) = \frac{1}{2}(x + 3)(x + 5)^2(x + 1)$.

2. Use finite differences to determine the degree of the polynomial function that fits the data. Then use technology to find the polynomial function.

x	−3	−2	−1	0	1	2
$f(x)$	68	34	16	8	4	−2

3. Find all the zeros of
$$f(x) = x^4 - 9x^3 + 24x^2 - 36x + 80.$$

In Exercises 4 and 5, find the real solution(s) of the equation. Round your answer to two decimal places, if necessary.

4. $3x^4 = 768$

5. $(x - 9)^3 = 162$

6. Let the graph of g be a translation 4 units right, followed by a vertical stretch by a factor of 2 of the graph of $f(x) = x^3 + 3x$. Write a rule for g.

7. Write an equation of the parabola in vertex form.

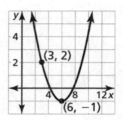

8. Write $(5 - 3i) + (8 + 6i) - 2i(i - 4)$ as a complex number in standard form.

9. The table shows the total costs of riding x miles in a taxi. What type of function can you use to model the data? Predict the total cost to ride 4 miles in the taxi.

Distance (miles), x	Total cost (dollars), y
1.5	3.75
2.0	4.00
2.5	4.25
3.0	4.50
3.5	4.75

5.1   Self-Assessment

Use the scale to rate your understanding of the learning target and the success criteria.

1 I do not understand.	2 I can do it with help.	3 I can do it on my own.	4 I can teach someone else.

	Rating	Date
5.1 *n*th Roots and Rational Exponents		
Learning Target: Evaluate expressions and solve equations containing *n*th roots and rational exponents.	1 2 3 4	
I can explain the meaning of a rational exponent.	1 2 3 4	
I can evaluate expressions with rational exponents.	1 2 3 4	
I can solve equations using *n*th roots.	1 2 3 4	

5.2 Extra Practice

In Exercises 1–4, use the properties of rational exponents to simplify the expression.

1. $\left(2^3 \cdot 3^3\right)^{-1/3}$

2. $\dfrac{10}{10^{-4/5}}$

3. $\left(\dfrac{52^5}{4^5}\right)^{1/6}$

4. $\dfrac{3^{1/3} \cdot 27^{2/3}}{8^{4/3}}$

In Exercises 5–7, use the properties of radicals to simplify the expression.

5. $\sqrt[6]{25} \cdot \sqrt[6]{625}$

6. $\dfrac{\sqrt{343}}{\sqrt{7}}$

7. $\dfrac{\sqrt[3]{25} \cdot \sqrt[3]{10}}{\sqrt[3]{2}}$

In Exercises 8–11, write the expression in simplest form.

8. $\sqrt[7]{384}$

9. $\sqrt[3]{\dfrac{5}{9}}$

10. $\dfrac{1}{4 - \sqrt{5}}$

11. $\dfrac{\sqrt{2}}{1 + \sqrt{6}}$

In Exercises 12–15, simplify the expression.

12. $-2\sqrt[3]{5} + 40\sqrt[3]{5}$

13. $2(1250)^{1/4} - 5(32)^{1/4}$

14. $\sqrt[5]{64a^{25}b^5}$

15. $\sqrt[6]{\dfrac{k}{h^{24}k^7}}$

In Exercises 16 and 17, write the expression in simplest form. Assume all variables are positive.

16. $\dfrac{\sqrt[4]{x} \cdot \sqrt[4]{81x}}{\sqrt[4]{16x^{36}}}$

17. $\dfrac{21\left(x^{-3/2}\right)\left(\sqrt{y}\right)\left(z^{5/2}\right)}{7^{-1}\sqrt{x}\left(y^{-1/2}\right)z}$

18. Find simplified expressions for the perimeter and area of the given figure.

$10x^{1/4}$

5.2 Review & Refresh

1. Let $f(x) = x^4 - 4x^3 + 3x$. Describe the graph of $g(x) = f(3x)$ as a transformation of the graph of f. Then write a rule for g.

In Exercises 2 and 3, identify the focus, directrix, and axis of symmetry of the parabola. Then graph the equation.

2. $y = -\frac{2}{3}x^2$

3. $y^2 = 12x$

4. Write the cubic function whose graph is shown.

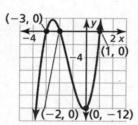

$(-3, 0)$
$(1, 0)$
$(-2, 0)$ $(0, -12)$

5. Is $f(x) = 3x - 9^{2x} + 6x^3$ a polynomial function? Explain.

6. Determine whether the sequence is *arithmetic*, *geometric*, or *neither*. Explain your reasoning.

6, 18, 54, 162, ...

In Exercises 7–10, simplify the expression.

7. $\left(\dfrac{45^{1/3}}{5^{1/3}}\right)^6$

8. $\sqrt[4]{4} \cdot \sqrt[4]{64}$

9. $\dfrac{1}{5 + \sqrt{2}}$

10. $\sqrt[3]{24} + 2\sqrt[3]{3}$

11. Determine whether $f(x) = 3x^5 - 4x^3$ is *even*, *odd*, or *neither*.

12. Evaluate $81^{3/4}$ without using technology.

13. While standing on a ladder, you drop a paintbrush from a height of 14 feet.

   a. Write a function h that gives the height (in feet) of the paintbrush after t seconds. How long does it take for the paintbrush to hit the ground?

   b. Find and interpret $h(0.25) - h(0.75)$.

5.2 Self-Assessment

Use the scale to rate your understanding of the learning target and the success criteria.

1 I do not understand.	**2** I can do it with help.	**3** I can do it on my own.	**4** I can teach someone else.

	Rating	Date
5.2 Properties of Rational Exponents and Radicals		
Learning Target: Simplify radical expressions.	1 2 3 4	
I can simplify expressions with rational exponents.	1 2 3 4	
I can explain when radical expressions are in simplest form.	1 2 3 4	
I can simplify variable expressions containing rational exponents and radicals.	1 2 3 4	

Name_____ Date _____

5.3 Extra Practice

In Exercises 1 and 2, graph the function. Find the domain and range of each function.

1. $f(x) = \sqrt[3]{-3x} + 1$

2. $g(x) = 2(x - 5)^{1/2} - 4$

In Exercises 3 and 4, describe the transformation of *f* represented by *g*. Then graph each function.

3. $f(x) = x^{1/3};\ g(x) = \frac{1}{5}(x + 2)^{1/3}$

4. $f(x) = \sqrt[4]{x};\ g(x) = -\sqrt[4]{2x} - 5$

5. Let g be a horizontal shrink by a factor of $\frac{5}{6}$, followed by a translation 10 units to the left of the graph of $f(x) = \sqrt[3]{15x + 1}$. Write a rule for g.

6. Use radical functions to graph $8x = y^2 + 5$. Identify the vertex and the direction that the parabola opens.

7. Use radical functions to graph $9x^2 + 9y^2 = 1$. Identify the radius and the intercepts.

8. The graph of a radical function f passes through the points $(-3, 0)$ and $(-2, 2)$. Write two different functions that can represent $f(x - 2) - 3$.

5.3 Review & Refresh

1. Solve $x^2 + 12x + 38 > 3$.

2. Write $\dfrac{16ab^{-2/3}}{8a^{1/2}b^{1/3}c^{-1/5}}$ in simplest form. Assume all variables are positive.

3. Use finite differences to determine the degree of the polynomial function that fits the data. Then use technology to find the polynomial function.

x	−4	−3	−2	−1	0	1
f(x)	95	47	16	−1	−7	−5

4. Evaluate $9^{2/5}$ using technology. Round your answer to two decimal places.

5. Graph $f(x) = -3\sqrt{x - 2}$. Find the domain and range of the function.

6. Solve $|x + 7| = 4x$.

7. Write a piecewise function represented by the graph.

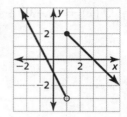

8. The prices of drones at a store have a median of $75 and a range of $120. The manager considers decreasing all the prices by either $15 or 10%. Which decrease results in a lesser median price? a lesser range of prices?

9. Describe the transformation of $f(x) = \sqrt[3]{x}$ represented by $g(x) = \sqrt[3]{x + 4} + 3$. Then graph each function.

5.3 Self-Assessment

Use the scale to rate your understanding of the learning target and the success criteria.

1	I do not understand.	2	I can do it with help.	3	I can do it on my own.	4	I can teach someone else.

	Rating	Date
5.3 Graphing Radical Functions		
Learning Target: Describe and graph transformations of radical functions.	1 2 3 4	
I can graph radical functions.	1 2 3 4	
I can describe transformations of radical functions.	1 2 3 4	
I can write functions that represent transformations of radical functions.	1 2 3 4	

Name_____ Date_____

5.4 Extra Practice

In Exercises 1–4, solve the equation. Check your solution.

1. $\sqrt{1-x}=7$

2. $\sqrt[3]{5x+1}=-4$

3. $\frac{1}{4}\sqrt[4]{2x}+6=10$

4. $2-\sqrt[4]{2x-6}=14$

5. The period P (in seconds) of a pendulum is given by the function $P=2\pi\sqrt{\dfrac{L}{32}}$, where L is the pendulum length (in feet). A pendulum has a period of 1.5 seconds. Find the pendulum length.

In Exercises 6–11, solve the equation. Check your solution(s).

6. $\sqrt[3]{432-27x^3}=3x$

7. $4\sqrt{x+1}=x+1$

8. $\sqrt{2x+2}-3\sqrt{x+1}=0$

9. $\sqrt{x+7}+2=\sqrt{3-x}$

10. $\frac{1}{2}x^{5/2}=16$

11. $(6x+10)^{7/3}+28=156$

In Exercises 12–14, solve the inequality.

12. $-4\sqrt{x-1}+3\geq-1$

13. $\sqrt[3]{\frac{2}{3}x+1}<6$

14. $2\sqrt{\frac{3}{4}x}-39\leq-25$

15. In basketball, the term "hang time" is the amount of time that a player is suspended in the air when making a basket. A player's hang time t (in seconds) is given by the function $t=0.5\sqrt{h}$, where h is the height (in feet) of the jump. In a slam-dunk contest, players try to maximize their hang time. The second-place finisher had a hang time of 1 second, and the winner had a hang time of 1.2 seconds. How many feet higher did the winner jump than the second-place finisher?

Name _____ Date _____

5.4 Review & Refresh

In Exercises 1 and 2, perform the operation.

1. $\left(3x^4 + 5x^3 - 7x\right) - \left(2x^4 - 3x^3\right)$

2. $\left(x^5 - 7x^4 + 12x^3 + 5x - 20\right) \div (x - 4)$

3. Write a rule for g.

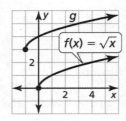

4. The graph of f is a parabola with axis of symmetry $x = -6$ that passes through the point $(-10, 4)$. Solve $f(x) = 4$. Explain your reasoning.

In Exercises 5 and 6, let $f(x) = x^3 + 3x^2 - 4$. Write a rule for g. Describe the graph of g as a transformation of the graph of f.

5. $g(x) = f(-x) - 2$ **6.** $g(x) = f\left(\frac{1}{2}x\right) + 6$

In Exercises 7–10, solve the inequality.

7. $3\sqrt{x + 2} < 12$ **8.** $5\sqrt[3]{x} - 6 \geq 19$

9. $-\sqrt[3]{x} + 7 \leq 9$ **10.** $-2\sqrt{x - 3} > -4$

11. The volume of a sphere is given by the equation $V = \dfrac{1}{6\sqrt{\pi}}S^{3/2}$, where S is the surface area of the sphere. Find the volume of a spherical weather balloon, to the nearest cubic meter, that has a surface area of 314 square meters. Use 3.14 for π.

12. Solve $4x^2 - 10x = 14$ by completing the square.

13. Solve the system using any method. Explain your choice of method.

$5x - 3y + z = -4$
$-x + 2y - 3z = 12$
$6x - 4y - z = 1$

5.4 Self-Assessment

Use the scale to rate your understanding of the learning target and the success criteria.

| 1 I do not understand. | 2 I can do it with help. | 3 I can do it on my own. | 4 I can teach someone else. |

	Rating	Date
5.4 Solving Radical Equations and Inequalities		
Learning Target: Solve equations and inequalities containing radicals and rational exponents.	1 2 3 4	
I can identify radical equations and inequalities.	1 2 3 4	
I can solve radical equations and inequalities.	1 2 3 4	
I can identify extraneous solutions of radical equations.	1 2 3 4	
I can solve real-life problems involving radical equations.	1 2 3 4	

Name_____ Date_____

5.5 Extra Practice

In Exercises 1–4, find $(f + g)(x)$ and $(f - g)(x)$ and state the domain of each. Then evaluate $f + g$ and $f - g$ for the given value of x.

1. $f(x) = -\frac{1}{2}\sqrt[3]{x}, g(x) = \frac{9}{2}\sqrt[3]{x}; x = -1000$

2. $f(x) = -x^2 - 3x + 8, g(x) = 6x - 3x^2; x = -1$

3. $f(x) = 4x^3 + 12, g(x) = 2x^2 - 3x^3 + 9; x = 2$

4. $f(x) = 5\sqrt[4]{x} + 1, g(x) = -3\sqrt[4]{x} - 2; x = 1$

In Exercises 5–8, find $(fg)(x)$ and $\left(\dfrac{f}{g}\right)(x)$ and state the domain of each. Then evaluate fg and $\dfrac{f}{g}$ for the given value of x.

5. $f(x) = -x^3, g(x) = 2\sqrt[3]{x}; x = -64$

6. $f(x) = 12x, g(x) = 11x^{1/2}; x = 4$

7. $f(x) = 0.25x^{1/3}, g(x) = -4x^{3/2}; x = 1$

8. $f(x) = 36x^{7/4}, g(x) = 4x^{1/2}; x = 16$

9. The growth of mold in Specimen A can be modeled by $A(t) = \frac{5}{6}t^{2/3}$. The growth of mold in Specimen B can be modeled by $B(t) = \frac{1}{3}t^{2/3}$.

   a. Find $(A - B)(t)$.

   b. Explain what $(A - B)(t)$ represents.

10. For the functions f and g, $(f + g)(-3) = -6$ and $\left(\dfrac{f}{g}\right)(-3) = -\dfrac{3}{4}$. Find $f(-3)$ and $g(-3)$.

5.5 Review & Refresh

In Exercises 1 and 2, solve the equation.

1. $4\sqrt{3x - 2} = 16$ **2.** $\sqrt{8 - 2x} = x$

3. Solve $\dfrac{5 + 3n}{2n} = 6a$ for n.

4. Determine whether the relation is a function. Explain.

$(3, -2), (4, 1), (5, -2), (8, 4)$

5. Let $f(x) = 6x^4$ and $g(x) = 3x^{2/3}$. Find $(fg)(x)$ and $\left(\dfrac{f}{g}\right)(x)$ and state the domain of each. Then evaluate fg and $\dfrac{f}{g}$ when $x = 8$.

6. Determine whether the table represents a *linear* or *nonlinear* function. Explain.

x	16	12	8	4
y	4	5	6	7

7. The net revenue R of an online store (in billions of dollars) can be modeled by $R = 2.83t^2 + 0.1t + 42$, where t represents the number of years after 2010.

   a. In what year did net revenue reach $150 billion?

   b. Find and interpret the average rate of change from 2010 to 2018.

   c. Do you think this model will be accurate after 30 years? Explain your reasoning.

5.5 Self-Assessment

Use the scale to rate your understanding of the learning target and the success criteria.

1	I do not understand.	2	I can do it with help.	3	I can do it on my own.	4	I can teach someone else.

	Rating	Date
5.5 Performing Function Operations		
Learning Target: Perform arithmetic operations on two functions.	1 2 3 4	
I can explain what it means to perform an arithmetic operation on two functions.	1 2 3 4	
I can find arithmetic combinations of two functions.	1 2 3 4	
I can state the domain of an arithmetic combination of two functions.	1 2 3 4	
I can evaluate an arithmetic combination of two functions for a given input.	1 2 3 4	

5.6   Extra Practice

In Exercises 1–6, let $f(x) = 3x + 1$, $g(x) = \sqrt{x + 2}$, and $h(x) = x^2 - 7$. Find the indicated value.

1. $f(g(7))$

2. $g(f(2))$

3. $h(f(-1))$

4. $g(h(-3))$

5. $f(f(1.4))$

6. $h\left(h\left(\frac{1}{2}\right)\right)$

In Exercises 7–12, find (a) $f(g(x))$, (b) $g(f(x))$, and (c) $f(f(x))$. State the domain of each composition.

7. $f(x) = 2x + 3, g(x) = |x - 1|$

8. $f(x) = 3x^2, g(x) = 3 - 4x$

9. $f(x) = 6x^{-1}, g(x) = 6x + 1$

10. $f(x) = 9x^{-1}, g(x) = x^2 - 4$

11. $f(x) = -2x + 5, g(x) = \sqrt{x - 9}$

12. $f(x) = 6x + 3, g(x) = \sqrt[3]{x + 7}$

13. The function $r(t) = 3t$ represents the radius (in feet) of an oil spill after t seconds. The area (in square feet) of the oil spill is represented by $A(r) = \pi r^2$.

   a. Find $A(r(t))$.

   b. Evaluate $A(r(6))$ and explain what it represents.

14. Show that the function $f(x) = 4\sqrt[3]{x - 3} + 4$ is a composition, in some order, of the functions $g, h, p,$ and q.

$$g(x) = 4x \qquad h(x) = x + 1 \qquad p(x) = x - 3 \qquad q(x) = \sqrt[3]{x}$$

Name _____ Date _____

In Exercises 1 and 2, solve the inequality.

1. $6\sqrt{x} + 4 \le 10$ **2.** $\sqrt[3]{x+5} - 2 > 7$

3. Describe the x-values for which (a) f is increasing or decreasing, (b) $f(x) > 0,$ and (c) $f(x) < 0.$

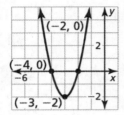

In Exercises 4 and 5, let $f(x) = 5 - x$ **and**

$g(x) = \dfrac{3x+4}{2}.$ **Find the indicated value.**

4. $f(g(4))$ **5.** $g(f(-3))$

6. Let g be a horizontal stretch by a factor of 6, followed by a translation 5 units down of the graph of $f(x) = \sqrt{12x}.$ Write a rule for $g.$

7. Solve the system using any method. Explain your choice of method.

$$-x^2 + 2x - y = -3$$
$$-2x + y = 2$$

8. From 2010 to 2018, the United States population (in millions) can be modeled by

$$P(t) = -0.027t^2 + 2.50t + 308.9$$

and the number of full-time employees can be modeled by

$$F(t) = -0.018t^3 + 0.29t^2 + 0.9t + 112$$

where t is the number of years since 2010. Find $(P - F)(t).$ Explain what $(P - F)(t)$ represents.

9. Find the volume of the cone. Round your answer to the nearest tenth.

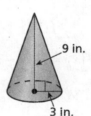

9 in.

3 in.

Use the scale to rate your understanding of the learning target and the success criteria.

| 1 | I do not understand. | 2 | I can do it with help. | 3 | I can do it on my own. | 4 | I can teach someone else. |

	Rating	Date
5.6 Composition of Functions		
Learning Target: Evaluate and find compositions of functions.	1 2 3 4	
I can evaluate a composition of functions.	1 2 3 4	
I can find a composition of functions.	1 2 3 4	
I can state the domain of a composition of functions.	1 2 3 4	

5.7   Extra Practice

In Exercises 1–3, find the inverse of the function. Then graph the function and its inverse.

1. $f(x) = 10x$

2. $f(x) = -\frac{1}{5}x - 7$

3. $f(x) = \frac{3}{4}x + \frac{5}{8}$

4. Determine whether the functions f and g are inverses. Explain your reasoning.

x	−4	−3	−2	−1	0	1
f(x)	17	13	9	5	1	−3

x	17	13	9	5	1	−3
g(x)	−4	−3	−2	−1	0	1

In Exercises 5 and 6, find the inverse of the function. Then graph the function and its inverse.

5. $f(x) = (x + 2)^3$

6. $f(x) = \frac{1}{3}x^4,\ x \geq 0$

In Exercises 7 and 8, determine whether the functions are inverse functions.

7. $f(x) = \dfrac{4x}{5} - 1,\ g(x) = \dfrac{5x + 1}{4}$

8. $f(x) = -(x - 2)^5 + 6,\ g(x) = 2 + (6 - x)^{1/5}$

9. The height h (in meters) of a dropped object after t seconds is represented by $h(t) = -4.9t^2 + 10$.

    a. Find the inverse function. Describe what it represents.

    b. After how many seconds will the object be 2 meters above the ground?

Name _____ Date _____

5.7 Review & Refresh

1. Describe the *x*-values for which the function is increasing, decreasing, positive, and negative.

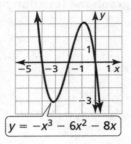

$y = -x^3 - 6x^2 - 8x$

In Exercises 2 and 3, find the inverse of the function. Then graph the function and its inverse.

2. $f(x) = \frac{1}{4}x^3 + 2$ 3. $f(x) = 2\sqrt{x - 3}$

4. Write a quadratic equation that has the given solutions.

$x = \dfrac{7 \pm \sqrt{37}}{6}$

5. Let $f(x) = -4\sqrt[3]{x}$ and $g(x) = 5\sqrt[3]{x}$. Find $(f + g)(x)$ and $(f - g)(x)$ and state the domain of each. Then evaluate $f + g$ and $f - g$ when $x = 27$.

6. Write an expression for the volume of the figure as a polynomial in standard form.

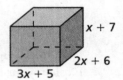

7. Write an equation of the parabola.

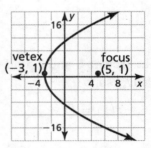

8. Let $f(x) = 4x + 1$ and $g(x) = \dfrac{1}{3x}$. Find $g(f(x))$ and state the domain.

5.7 Self-Assessment

Use the scale to rate your understanding of the learning target and the success criteria.

| 1 | I do not understand. | 2 | I can do it with help. | 3 | I can do it on my own. | 4 | I can teach someone else. |

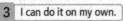

	Rating	Date
5.7 Inverse of a Function		
Learning Target: Understand the relationship between inverse functions.	1 2 3 4	
I can explain what inverse functions are.	1 2 3 4	
I can find inverses of linear and nonlinear functions.	1 2 3 4	
I can determine whether a pair of functions are inverses.	1 2 3 4	

84 Algebra 2
Practice Workbook and Test Prep

Copyright © Big Ideas Learning, LLC
All rights reserved.

Name_____ Date_____

Chapter Self-Assessment

Use the scale to rate your understanding of the learning target and the success criteria.

| 1 I do not understand. | 2 I can do it with help. | 3 I can do it on my own. | 4 I can teach someone else. |

	Rating	Date
Chapter 5 Rational Exponents and Radical Functions		
Learning Target: Understand rational exponents and radical functions.	1 2 3 4	
I can represent roots using rational exponents.	1 2 3 4	
I can describe the properties of rational exponents and radicals.	1 2 3 4	
I can solve radical equations and inequalities.	1 2 3 4	
I can find compositions and inverses of functions.	1 2 3 4	
5.1 nth Roots and Rational Exponents		
Learning Target: Evaluate expressions and solve equations containing nth roots and rational exponents.	1 2 3 4	
I can explain the meaning of a rational exponent.	1 2 3 4	
I can evaluate expressions with rational exponents.	1 2 3 4	
I can solve equations using nth roots.	1 2 3 4	
5.2 Properties of Rational Exponents and Radicals		
Learning Target: Simplify radical expressions.	1 2 3 4	
I can simplify expressions with rational exponents.	1 2 3 4	
I can explain when radical expressions are in simplest form.	1 2 3 4	
I can simplify variable expressions containing rational exponents and radicals.	1 2 3 4	
5.3 Graphing Radical Functions		
Learning Target: Describe and graph transformations of radical functions.	1 2 3 4	
I can graph radical functions.	1 2 3 4	
I can describe transformations of radical functions.	1 2 3 4	
I can write functions that represent transformations of radical functions.	1 2 3 4	

Chapter 5

Chapter Self-Assessment (continued)

	Rating	Date
5.4 Solving Radical Equations and Inequalities		
Learning Target: Solve equations and inequalities containing radicals and rational exponents.	1 2 3 4	
I can identify radical equations and inequalities.	1 2 3 4	
I can solve radical equations and inequalities.	1 2 3 4	
I can identify extraneous solutions of radical equations.	1 2 3 4	
I can solve real-life problems involving radical equations.	1 2 3 4	
5.5 Performing Function Operations		
Learning Target: Perform arithmetic operations on two functions.	1 2 3 4	
I can explain what it means to perform arithmetic operations on two functions.	1 2 3 4	
I can find arithmetic combinations of two functions.	1 2 3 4	
I can state the domain of an arithmetic combination of two functions.	1 2 3 4	
I can evaluate an arithmetic combination of two functions for a given input.	1 2 3 4	
5.6 Composition of Functions		
Learning Target: Evaluate and find compositions of functions.	1 2 3 4	
I can evaluate a composition of functions.	1 2 3 4	
I can find a composition of functions.	1 2 3 4	
I can state the domain of a composition of functions.	1 2 3 4	
5.7 Inverse of a Function		
Learning Target: Understand the relationship between inverse functions.	1 2 3 4	
I can explain what inverse functions are.	1 2 3 4	
I can find inverses of linear and nonlinear functions.	1 2 3 4	
I can determine whether a pair of functions are inverses.	1 2 3 4	

Chapter 5 Test Prep

1. Which of the following correctly describes the degree and leading coefficient of f?

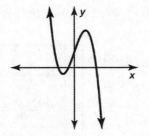

Ⓐ The degree is even and the leading coefficient is positive.

Ⓑ The degree is even and the leading coefficient is negative.

Ⓒ The degree is odd and the leading coefficient is positive.

Ⓓ The degree is odd and the leading coefficient is negative.

2. Write the inverse of $f(x) = \sqrt[3]{2x - 4}$.

_____

3. Which equation has a graph that is a line passing through the point $(-2, 3)$ and is perpendicular to the graph of $y = \frac{1}{2}x - 3$?

Ⓐ $y = -2x - 1$

Ⓑ $y = 2x + 7$

Ⓒ $y = -\frac{1}{2}x + 2$

Ⓓ $y = -2x + 4$

4. Which of the following could be a rule for g?

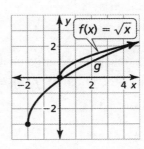

Ⓐ $g(x) = \sqrt{x + 2} - 3$

Ⓑ $g(x) = \sqrt{x - 2} - 3$

Ⓒ $g(x) = 2\sqrt{x + 2} - 3$

Ⓓ $g(x) = 2\sqrt{x - 2} - 3$

Chapter 5 — Test Prep (continued)

5. Let $f(x) = 3x^{5/3}$ and $g(x) = -2x^{5/3}$. Evaluate $(f - g)(-8)$.

$(f - g)(-8) =$

6. According to the Rational Root Theorem, which is *not* a possible zero of the function $f(x) = 10x^4 - 3x^3 + 2x^2 - 4x + 8$?

Ⓐ -2

Ⓑ $-\dfrac{5}{4}$

Ⓒ $\dfrac{1}{2}$

Ⓓ 1

7. Let the graph of g be a translation 2 units up and 2 units right, followed by a reflection in the y-axis of the graph of $f(x) = -(x + 3)^2 - 2$. Which of the following is a rule for g?

Ⓐ $g(x) = -(-x + 5)^2$

Ⓑ $g(x) = (x + 5)^2$

Ⓒ $g(x) = -(-x + 1)^2$

Ⓓ $g(x) = (x + 1)^2$

Chapter 5 Test Prep (continued)

8. The speed s (in miles per hour) of a vehicle just before the brakes are applied can be estimated by using the formula $s = \sqrt{28.75d}$, where d is the length (in feet) of the skid marks the vehicle leaves. You are driving 30 miles per hour when an animal jumps in front of your car. Estimate the length of your skid mark to the nearest tenth.

   Ⓐ 1.0 foot

   Ⓑ 2.1 feet

   Ⓒ 29.4 feet

   Ⓓ 31.3 feet

9. Select all the equivalent expressions.

   Ⓐ $\left(6^{3/8}\right)^{2/3}$

   Ⓑ $\dfrac{6^{3/4}}{6}$

   Ⓒ $\left(\sqrt[8]{6}\right)^2$

   Ⓓ $\dfrac{\sqrt[4]{12}}{\sqrt[4]{2}}$

   Ⓔ $\sqrt[4]{768} + \sqrt[4]{48}$

   Ⓕ $\sqrt[4]{486} - \sqrt[4]{96}$

10. For the system shown, what is the value of $y - x$?

    $$x^2 + y = 3$$
    $$y - 5 = x^2 + 4x$$

    $y - x =$

11. Let $f(x) = 2x^2 - 5$ and $g(x) = 4 - x$. What is $f(g(x)) - g(f(x))$?

    Ⓐ $2x^2 - 2x - 6$

    Ⓑ $4x^2 - 16x + 18$

    Ⓒ $16x - 18$

    Ⓓ $-16x + 36$

12. Between which two consecutive integers does $\sqrt[3]{1330}$ lie?

Ⓐ 10 and 11

Ⓑ 11 and 12

Ⓒ 36 and 37

Ⓓ 37 and 38

13. A parabola has a vertex at $(-1, -3)$ and passes through the point $(3, 45)$. Write an equation for the parabola in vertex form.

_____

14. The table shows the inputs and outputs of two functions. Select all the true statements.

x	−3	−2	−1	0	1	2
f(x)	1	−3	3	2	4	5
g(x)	0	1	−3	−7	−2	−1

Ⓐ $g(f(0)) = 5$

Ⓑ $f(g(2)) = 3$

Ⓒ $f(f(-2)) = 1$

Ⓓ $g(g(-3)) = -7$

Ⓔ $f(g(g(1))) = 4$

15. You complete the square for an expression of the form $x^2 + bx$, where $b > 0$, by adding 144. What is the value of b?

$b =$

16. Find the values of a, b, and c so that the linear system shown has $(0, -4, -2)$ as its only solution.

$$3x - 3y + z = a$$
$$3x + 2y - 3z = b$$
$$-3x + z = c$$

Ⓐ $a = -10$, $b = 2$, and $c = 2$

Ⓑ $a = 2$, $b = 8$, and $c = -4$

Ⓒ $a = 10$, $b = -2$, and $c = -2$

Ⓓ $a = 10$, $b = -2$, and $c = -4$

Name_____ Date_____

6.1 Extra Practice

In Exercises 1–4, determine whether the function represents *exponential growth* or *exponential decay*. Then graph the function.

1. $y = \left(\frac{1}{12}\right)^x$

2. $y = \left(\frac{7}{2}\right)^x$

3. $y = (1.4)^x$

4. $y = (0.8)^x$

5. The number of bacteria y (in thousands) in a culture can be approximated by the model $y = 100(1.99)^t$, where t is the number of hours the culture is incubated.

   a. Tell whether the model represents *exponential growth* or *exponential decay*.

   b. Identify the hourly percent increase or decrease in the number of bacteria.

   c. Estimate when the number of bacteria will be 1,000,000.

In Exercises 6 and 7, rewrite the function in the form $y = a(1 + r)^t$ or $y = a(1 - r)^t$. State the growth or decay rate, and describe the end behavior of the function.

6. $y = a\left(\frac{3}{2}\right)^{t/7}$

7. $y = a(0.9)^{4t}$

8. You deposit $1250 in an account that pays 1.25% annual interest. Find the balance after 5 years when the interest is compounded daily.

9. You buy a new smartphone for $700 and sell it 2 years later for $185. Assume that the resale value of the smartphone decays exponentially with time. Write an equation that represents the resale value V (in dollars) of the smartphone as a function of the time t (in years) since it was purchased.

Name _____ Date _____

1. Simplify $\left(7x^3 \cdot 4x^6\right)^2$.

2. In the exponential model $y = 5.8(0.6)^x$, identify the initial amount, the growth or decay factor, and the percent increase or decrease.

3. Determine whether $f(x) = \frac{1}{7}x + 4$ and $g(x) = 7x - 28$ are inverse functions.

4. Let $f(x) = 3x^4$ and $g(x) = \sqrt[3]{x}$. Find $(fg)(x)$ and $\left(\dfrac{f}{g}\right)(x)$ and state the domain of each. Then evaluate $(fg)(8)$ and $\left(\dfrac{f}{g}\right)(8)$.

5. Let $g(x) = -\frac{1}{3}x + 2$ and $h(x) = 3x^{-1}$. Find $g\big(h(x)\big)$ and state the domain.

In Exercises 6 and 7, determine whether the function represents *exponential growth* or *exponential decay*. Then graph the function.

6. $y = (2.5)^x$

7. $y = \left(\dfrac{2}{3}\right)^x$

8. The times (in hours) spent online last night by a group of friends, are shown.

   1.5, 7, 0, 1, 3, 2, 2.5

   a. Make a box-and-whisker plot that represents the data. Describe the shape of the distribution.

   b. Does the data contain any outliers? If so, explain how the outlier(s) affect the mean and five-number summary.

6.1 Self-Assessment

Use the scale to rate your understanding of the learning target and the success criteria.

| 1 | I do not understand. | 2 | I can do it with help. | 3 | I can do it on my own. | 4 | I can teach someone else. |

	Rating	Date
6.1 Exponential Growth and Decay Functions		
Learning Target: Write and graph exponential growth and decay functions.	1 2 3 4	
I can identify and graph exponential growth and decay functions.	1 2 3 4	
I can write exponential growth and decay functions.	1 2 3 4	
I can solve real-life problems using exponential growth and decay functions.	1 2 3 4	

6.2 Extra Practice

In Exercises 1–4, simplify the expression.

1. $e^{-9} \cdot e^{12}$

2. $\dfrac{25e^2}{35e^7}$

3. $\sqrt[4]{16e^{24x}}$

4. $\left(2e^{-3x}\right)^5 \cdot 2e^{x+1}$

In Exercises 5–8, determine whether the function represents *exponential growth* or *exponential decay*. Then graph the function.

5. $y = 4e^{-2x}$

6. $y = 0.75e^{4x}$

7. $y = 5e^{0.25x}$

8. $y = 0.8e^{-3x}$

In Exercises 9 and 10, use a table of values or technology to graph the function. Then find the domain and range.

9. $y = e^x - 4$

10. $y = 2e^{x+3}$

11. You and your friend each have an account that earns annual interest compounded continuously. The balance A (in dollars) of your account after t years can be modeled by $A = 3800e^{0.05t}$. The graph shows the balance of your friend's account over time. Which account has a greater principal? Which account has a greater balance after 15 years?

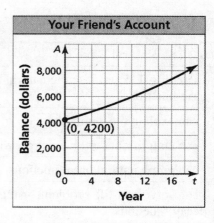

Name _____ Date _____

In Exercises 1 and 2, write the number in scientific notation.

1. 540,000,000   2. 0.000092

3. Graph $y = -2(x + 1)(x - 1)$. Label the vertex and axis of symmetry.

4. Write the cubic function whose graph is shown.

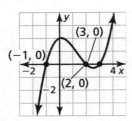

5. When the polynomial $f(x)$ is divided by $x + 5$, the remainder is 4. Find one point on the graph of $y = f(x)$.

In Exercises 6 and 7, determine whether the function represents *exponential growth* or *exponential decay*. Then graph the function.

6. $y = e^{0.2x}$ 7. $f(x) = 2e^{-3x}$

8. The function $C(g) = 2.75g$ represents the cost (in dollars) for g gallons of gasoline at a gas station. The function $g(t) = 1.5t$ approximates the number of gallons of gasoline a lawn mower uses after t hours.

   a. Find $C(g(t))$. Interpret the coefficient.

   b. Evaluate $C(g(4))$ and explain what it represents.

6.2 Self-Assessment

Use the scale to rate your understanding of the learning target and the success criteria.

| 1 I do not understand. | 2 I can do it with help. | 3 I can do it on my own. | 4 I can teach someone else. |

	Rating	Date
6.2 The Natural Base *e*		
Learning Target: Use the natural base *e* and graph natural base functions.	1 2 3 4	
I can explain the natural base *e*.	1 2 3 4	
I can simplify natural base expressions.	1 2 3 4	
I can graph natural base functions.	1 2 3 4	
I can solve real-life problems using exponential growth and decay functions.	1 2 3 4	

Name_____ Date_____

6.3 Extra Practice

In Exercises 1–4, rewrite the equation in exponential form.

1. $\log_{10} 1000 = 3$ **2.** $\log_5 \frac{1}{25} = -2$ **3.** $\log_{10} 1 = 0$ **4.** $\log_{1/4} 64 = -3$

In Exercises 5–8, rewrite the equation in logarithmic form.

5. $12^2 = 144$ **6.** $20^{-1} = \frac{1}{20}$ **7.** $216^{1/3} = 6$ **8.** $4^0 = 1$

In Exercises 9–12, evaluate the logarithm.

9. $\log_4 256$ **10.** $\log_{1/8} 1$ **11.** $\log_2 \frac{1}{32}$ **12.** $\log_{25} 0.2$

In Exercises 13 and 14, simplify the expression.

13. $13^{\log_{13} 6}$ **14.** $\ln e^{x^3}$

In Exercises 15 and 16, find the inverse of the function.

15. $y = 15^x + 10$ **16.** $y = \ln 2x - 8$

In Exercises 17 and 18, graph the function.

17. $y = \log_2(x + 1)$ **18.** $y = \log_{1/2} x - 4$

19. Evaluate each logarithm. (*Hint:* For each logarithm, $\log_b x$, rewrite b and x as powers of the same base.)

a. $\log_{16} 64$ **b.** $\log_{81} 27$ **c.** $\log_{16} 32$ **d.** $\log_{27} 243$

Name _____ Date _____

In Exercises 1 and 2, identify the function family to which f belongs. Compare the graph of f to the graph of its parent function.

1.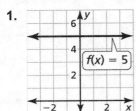

   $f(x) = 5$

2.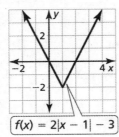

   $f(x) = 2|x - 1| - 3$

In Exercises 3–6, simplify the expression.

3. $e^6 \cdot e^3$

4. $\dfrac{8e^7}{16e^8}$

5. $\left(5e^x\right)^2$

6. $\sqrt[3]{8e^{12x}}$

In Exercises 7 and 8, solve the equation.

7. $0 = x^2 - 7x - 30$ 8. $n^2 - 12n = 0$

9. Find the real solution(s) of $x^3 = -216$.

10. The two-way table shows the results of a survey. Find and interpret the marginal frequencies.

		Like Dogs	
		Yes	No
Like Cats	Yes	16	9
	No	10	3

In Exercises 11 and 12, graph the function.

11. $y = 2 + \log_3 x$ 12. $f(x) = \log_5(x + 3)$

13. The volume of the pyramid-shaped candle is 364 cubic inches. What is the height of the candle?

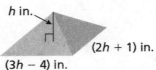

h in.

$(2h + 1)$ in.

$(3h - 4)$ in.

Use the scale to rate your understanding of the learning target and the success criteria.

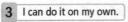

| 1 | I do not understand. | 2 | I can do it with help. | 3 | I can do it on my own. | 4 | I can teach someone else. |

	Rating	Date
6.3 Logarithms and Logarithmic Functions		
Learning Target: Understand logarithms and graph logarithmic functions.	1 2 3 4	
I can explain the meaning of a logarithm with base b.	1 2 3 4	
I can evaluate logarithmic expressions.	1 2 3 4	
I can graph logarithmic functions.	1 2 3 4	

6.4 Extra Practice

In Exercises 1–6, describe the transformation of *f* represented by *g*. Then graph each function.

1. $f(x) = 6^x$, $g(x) = 6^x + 6$

2. $f(x) = e^x$, $g(x) = e^{x-4}$

3. $f(x) = \left(\frac{1}{5}\right)^x$, $g(x) = \left(\frac{1}{5}\right)^{-3x} + 4$

4. $f(x) = \log_5 x$, $g(x) = \frac{1}{2}\log_5(x + 7)$

5. $f(x) = \log_{1/3} x$, $g(x) = \log_{1/3} x - \frac{4}{3}$

6. $f(x) = \log x$, $g(x) = -3\log(x - 2)$

7. Let the graph of *g* be a reflection in the *y*-axis, followed by a translation 5 units down of the graph of $f(x) = 8^x$. Write a rule for *g*.

8. Let the graph of *g* be a translation 6 units right and 7 units up of the graph of $f(x) = \log_{1/4} x$. Write a rule for *g*.

9. Write a logarithmic function whose graph has a *x*-intercept of 6 and an asymptote of $x = -4$.

Name _____ Date _____

6.4 Review & Refresh

In Exercises 1–4, simplify the expression.

1. $7^{\log_7 x}$

2. $e^{\ln 12}$

3. $\log_8 8^{11x}$

4. $10^{\log(2x + 7)}$

5. Determine whether the data shows a linear relationship. If so, write an equation of a line of fit. Then estimate y when $x = 8$ and explain its meaning in the context of the situation.

Time (hours), x	1	3	5	7
Pages read, y	45	135	225	315

In Exercises 6 and 7, write a rule for g that represents the indicated transformation of the graph of f.

6. $f(x) = e^x$; horizontal stretch by a factor of 4, followed by a translation 2 units up

7. $f(x) = \log_4 x$; reflection in the x-axis followed by a translation 5 units left

8. Solve $\sqrt{2x - 6} = 8$. Check your solution.

9. Account A and Account B earn annual interest compounded continuously. The balance B (in dollars) of Account A after t years is modeled by $B = 200e^{0.04t}$. The graph shows the balance of Account B. Which account has a greater principal? Which account has a greater balance after 8 years?

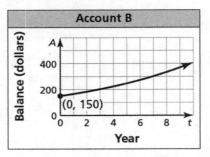

10. Rewrite $y = a\left(\dfrac{1}{3}\right)^{3t}$ in the form $y = a(1 + r)^t$ or $y = a(1 - r)^t$. State the growth or decay rate, and describe the end behavior of the function.

6.4 Self-Assessment

Use the scale to rate your understanding of the learning target and the success criteria.

1 I do not understand.	**2** I can do it with help.	**3** I can do it on my own.	**4** I can teach someone else.

	Rating	Date
6.4 Transformations of Exponential and Logarithmic Functions		
Learning Target: Describe and graph transformations of exponential and logarithmic functions.	1 2 3 4	
I can describe transformations of exponential and logarithmic functions.	1 2 3 4	
I can graph transformations of exponential and logarithmic functions.	1 2 3 4	
I can write functions that represent transformations of exponential and logarithmic functions.	1 2 3 4	

Name_____ Date_____

6.5 Extra Practice

In Exercises 1–4, use log$_2$ 5 ≈ 2.322 and log$_2$ 12 ≈ 3.585 to evaluate the logarithm.

1. $\log_2 60$

2. $\log_2 \frac{1}{144}$

3. $\log_2 \frac{12}{25}$

4. $\log_2 720$

In Exercises 5–8, expand the logarithmic expression.

5. $\log 10x$

6. $\ln 2x^6$

7. $\log_3 \frac{x^4}{3y^3}$

8. $\ln \sqrt[4]{3y^2}$

In Exercises 9–13, condense the logarithmic expression.

9. $\log_2 3 + \log_2 8$

10. $\log_5 4 - 2 \log_5 5$

11. $3 \ln 6x + \ln 4y$

12. $\log_2 625 - \log_2 125 + \frac{1}{3} \log_2 27$

13. $-\log_6 6 - \log_6 2y + 2 \log_6 3x$

In Exercises 14–17, use the change-of-base formula to evaluate the logarithm.

14. $\log_3 17$

15. $\log_9 294$

16. $\log_7 \frac{4}{9}$

17. $\log_6 \frac{1}{10}$

18. The intensity of the sound of a certain children's television show is half the intensity of the adult show that is on before it. Use the function $L(I) = 10 \log \dfrac{I}{I_0}$ to determine the loudness decrease (in decibels).

19. Hick's Law states that given n equally probable choices, such as choices on a menu, the average human's reaction time T (in seconds) required to choose from those choices is approximately $T = a + b \log_2(n + 1)$, where a and b are constants.

   a. Show that the given function can be written in terms of common logarithms as
   $$T = a + \frac{\log(n + 1)^b}{\log 2}.$$

   b. If $a = 4$ and $b = 1$, how much longer would it take a customer to choose what to eat from a menu of 40 items than from a menu of 10 items?

Name _____ Date _____

In Exercises 1 and 2, rewrite the equation in exponential or logarithmic form.

1. $\log_6 1296 = 4$ 2. $8^5 = 32{,}768$

3. Write an equation of the parabola in vertex form.

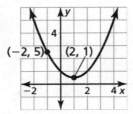

$(-2, 5)$ $(2, 1)$

4. Use the change-of-base formula to evaluate $\log_4 12$.

In Exercises 5 and 6, solve the equation by graphing.

5. $x^2 + 3x - 1 = -2x^2 + 3x + 5$

6. $-(x + 4)(x + 1) = x^2 - 2x$

7. At a movie theater, three small popcorns, two medium popcorns, and one large popcorn cost $43.20. One small popcorn, three medium popcorns, and one large popcorn cost $37.95. One small popcorn, one medium popcorn, and four large popcorns cost $47.05. How much does each popcorn size cost?

8. Solve $x^2 - x - 12 < 0$ by graphing.

9. Expand $\log \dfrac{y^9}{x^8}$.

10. The graph of g is a transformation of the graph of $f(x) = 2^x$. Write a rule for g.

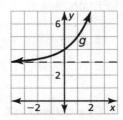

g

In Exercises 11 and 12, perform the operation. Write the answer in standard form.

11. $(5 - 3i)(2 - 7i)$ 12. $(6 + 2i) - (8 - i)$

In Exercises 13–16, simplify the expression.

13. $e^9 \cdot e^7$ 14. $\dfrac{12e^6}{4e^2}$

15. $\left(3e^{5x}\right)^4$ 16. $\dfrac{e^8 \cdot e^{-4}}{e^{10}}$

Use the scale to rate your understanding of the learning target and the success criteria.

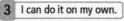

| 1 | I do not understand. | 2 | I can do it with help. | 3 | I can do it on my own. | 4 | I can teach someone else. |

	Rating	Date
6.5 Properties of Logarithms		
Learning Target: Use properties of logarithms.	1 2 3 4	
I can evaluate logarithms.	1 2 3 4	
I can expand or condense logarithmic expressions.	1 2 3 4	
I can explain how to use the change-of-base formula.	1 2 3 4	

6.6 Extra Practice

In Exercises 1–6, solve the equation.

1. $5^{2x+4} = 5^{5x-8}$

2. $4^{2x-1} = 8^{x+2}$

3. $3^{x+3} = 5$

4. $\left(\frac{1}{5}\right)^{3x-2} = \sqrt{25^x}$

5. $12e^{1-x} = 500$

6. $-14 + 3e^x = 11$

7. You buy juice for your graduation party and leave it in your hot car. When you take the juice out of the car and move it into the basement, the temperature of the juice is 80°F. When the room temperature of the basement is 60°F, the cooling rate is $r = 0.0147$. Using Newton's Law of Cooling, $T = (T_0 - T_R)e^{-rt} + T_R$, to determine how long will it take to cool the juice to 63°F.

In Exercises 8–12, solve the equation. Check your solution(s).

8. $2 = \log_3 4x$

9. $\ln(x^2 + 3) = \ln 4$

10. $\log_8(x^2 - 5) = \frac{2}{3}$

11. $\ln x + \ln(x + 2) = \ln(x + 6)$

12. $\log_2(x + 5) - \log_2(x - 2) = 3$

In Exercises 13–16, solve the inequality.

13. $25^x > \frac{1}{5}$

14. $\ln 4 \geq \ln(x + 8)$

15. $\log x \leq \frac{1}{2}$

16. $e^{2x-5} < 14$

17. A drone sells for $200. The value of the drone decreases by 15% each year. When does the value of the drone exceed $144.50?

In Exercises 18 and 19, solve the equation.

18. $3^{2x} - 8 \cdot 3^x + 15 = 0$

19. $4^{2x} + 3 \cdot 4^x - 28 = 0$

Name _____ Date _____

1. The intensity of the sound of a rock concert is 12 times greater than the intensity of the loudest volume setting on your tablet. Use the function $L(I) = 10 \log \dfrac{I}{I_0}$ to determine the loudness increase (in decibels).

2. Describe the transformation of $f(x) = e^x$ represented by $g(x) = e^{x+3}$. Then graph each function.

5. For the functions f and g, $\left(\dfrac{f}{g}\right)(3) = 5$ and $(f + g)(3) = 18$. Find the values of $f(3)$ and $g(3)$.

6. Solve $x^2 - 4x + 1 = 0$.

In Exercises 7 and 8, solve the equation. Check your solution(s).

7. $\log_2 x + \log_2(x + 3) = 4$

8. $\log_3 4x^2 + \log_3 8 = 2$

In Exercises 9 and 10, evaluate the logarithm.

9. $\log_4 1024$ 10. $\log_{1/4} 64$

11. Use the table to find the product of $2x^2 - 3x + 4$ and $3x - 5$.

	$2x^2$	$-3x$	4
3x		$-9x^2$	$12x$
-5	$-10x^2$		

In Exercises 3 and 4, simplify the expression.

3. $9\sqrt[3]{15} + 2\sqrt[3]{15}$ 4. $\sqrt[4]{\dfrac{m^8}{n^4}}$

Use the scale to rate your understanding of the learning target and the success criteria.

| 1 | I do not understand. | 2 | I can do it with help. | 3 | I can do it on my own. | 4 | I can teach someone else. |

	Rating	Date
6.6 Solving Exponential and Logarithmic Equations		
Learning Target: Solve exponential and logarithmic equations and inequalities.	1 2 3 4	
I can solve exponential equations.	1 2 3 4	
I can solve logarithmic equations.	1 2 3 4	
I can solve exponential and logarithmic inequalities.	1 2 3 4	

6.7 Extra Practice

In Exercises 1 and 2, determine the type of function represented by the table. Explain your reasoning.

1.

x	6	7	8	9	10	11
y	34	47	62	79	98	119

2.

x	−5	−3	−1	1	3	5
y	$\frac{1}{5}$	$\frac{3}{5}$	$\frac{9}{5}$	$\frac{27}{5}$	$\frac{81}{5}$	$\frac{243}{5}$

In Exercises 3–6, write an exponential function $y = ab^x$ whose graph passes through the given points.

3. $(1, 12), (3, 108)$

4. $(-1, 2), (3, 32)$

5. $(2, 9), (4, 324)$

6. $(-2, 2), (1, 0.25)$

7. An Olympic swimmer starts selling a new type of goggles. The table shows the number y of goggles sold during a 6-month period. Create a scatter plot of the data pairs $(x, \ln y)$ to show that an exponential model should be a good fit for the original data pairs (x, y). Then write an exponential model for the original data.

Months, x	1	2	3	4	5	6
Goggles sold, y	28	47	64	79	97	107

8. The table shows the height h (in feet) of a tree at specific ages t (in years). Use technology to find a logarithmic model of the form $h = a + b \ln t$ that represents the data. Estimate the height when the tree is 9 years old.

Age, t	1	3	5	7	11	13
Height, h	2.5	13.5	18	21.5	24	24.5

Name _____ Date _____

1. Let $y = \dfrac{x}{8}$. Tell whether x and y are in a proportional relationship. Explain your reasoning.

2. You cook a hamburger until the internal temperature reaches $160°F$. The hamburger is placed on a plate until the internal temperature reaches $100°F$ and can be eaten. When the room temperature is $75°F$, the cooling rate of the hamburger is $r = 0.2448$. How long do you have to wait until you can eat the hamburger?

3. Use the change of base formula to evaluate $\log_7 \dfrac{3}{4}$.

In Exercises 4 and 5, write an exponential function $y = ab^x$ whose graph passes through the given points.

4. $(2, 18), (4, 648)$ 5. $(-1, 2), (3, 18)$

6. Identify the focus, directrix, and axis of symmetry of $y^2 = \dfrac{2}{3}x$. Graph the equation.

In Exercises 7 and 8, solve the equation.

7. $e^{3x} = e^{4x-9}$ 8. $\ln(6x + 2) = \ln 5$

9. Show that $x + 4$ is a factor of $f(x) = x^3 + 3x^2 - 6x - 8$. Then factor $f(x)$ completely.

10. Complete the square for $x^2 - 8x$. Then factor the trinomial.

Use the scale to rate your understanding of the learning target and the success criteria.

| 1 | I do not understand. | 2 | I can do it with help. | 3 | I can do it on my own. | 4 | I can teach someone else. |

	Rating	Date
6.7 Modeling with Exponential and Logarithmic Functions		
Learning Target: Write exponential and logarithmic functions to model sets of data.	1 2 3 4	
I can use a common ratio to determine whether data can be represented by an exponential function.	1 2 3 4	
I can write an exponential function using two points.	1 2 3 4	
I can use technology to find exponential models and logarithmic models for sets of data.	1 2 3 4	

Name_____ Date_____

Chapter Self-Assessment

Use the scale to rate your understanding of the learning target and the success criteria.

| 1 | I do not understand. | 2 | I can do it with help. | 3 | I can do it on my own. | 4 | I can teach someone else. |

	Rating	Date
Chapter 6 Exponential and Logarithmic Functions		
Learning Target: Understand exponential and logarithmic functions.	1 2 3 4	
I can determine whether a function represents exponential growth or decay.	1 2 3 4	
I can simplify exponential and logarithmic expressions.	1 2 3 4	
I can solve exponential and logarithmic equations.	1 2 3 4	
I can model exponential and logarithmic functions.	1 2 3 4	
6.1 Exponential Growth and Decay Functions		
Learning Target: Write and graph exponential growth and decay functions.	1 2 3 4	
I can identify and graph exponential growth and decay functions.	1 2 3 4	
I can write exponential growth and decay functions.	1 2 3 4	
I can solve real-life problems using exponential growth and decay functions.	1 2 3 4	
6.2 The Natural Base e		
Learning Target: Use the natural base e and graph natural base functions.	1 2 3 4	
I can explain the natural base e.	1 2 3 4	
I can simplify natural base expressions.	1 2 3 4	
I can graph natural base functions.	1 2 3 4	
I can solve real-life problems using exponential growth and decay functions.	1 2 3 4	
6.3 Logarithms and Logarithmic Functions		
Learning Target: Understand logarithms and graph logarithmic functions.	1 2 3 4	
I can explain the meaning of a logarithm with base b.	1 2 3 4	
I can evaluate logarithmic expressions.	1 2 3 4	
I can graph logarithmic functions.	1 2 3 4	

Chapter Self-Assessment (continued)

	Rating	Date
6.4 Transformations of Exponential and Logarithmic Functions		
Learning Target: Describe and graph transformations of exponential and logarithmic functions.	1 2 3 4	
I can describe transformations of exponential and logarithmic functions.	1 2 3 4	
I can graph transformations of exponential and logarithmic functions.	1 2 3 4	
I can write functions that represent transformations of exponential and logarithmic functions.	1 2 3 4	
6.5 Properties of Logarithms		
Learning Target: Use properties of logarithms.	1 2 3 4	
I can evaluate logarithms.	1 2 3 4	
I can expand or condense logarithmic expressions.	1 2 3 4	
I can explain how to use the change-of-base formula.	1 2 3 4	
6.6 Solving Exponential and Logarithmic Equations		
Learning Target: Solve exponential and logarithmic equations and inequalities.	1 2 3 4	
I can solve exponential equations.	1 2 3 4	
I can solve logarithmic equations.	1 2 3 4	
I can solve exponential and logarithmic inequalities.	1 2 3 4	
6.7 Modeling with Exponential and Logarithmic Functions		
Learning Target: Write exponential and logarithmic functions to model sets of data.	1 2 3 4	
I can use a common ratio to determine whether data can be represented by an exponential function.	1 2 3 4	
I can write an exponential function using two points.	1 2 3 4	
I can use technology to find exponential models and logarithmic models for sets of data.	1 2 3 4	

Chapter 6 Test Prep

1. Let $f(x) = x - 3$ and $g(x) = -x^2 + 7$. Evaluate $f(g(-4))$.

$f(g(-4)) =$

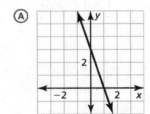

2. Solve $\ln(2x + 3) = \ln(5x - 6)$.

$x =$

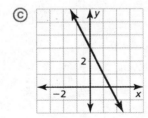

3. Let $f(x) = x$ and $g(x) = -2f(x) + 3$. Which of the following correctly shows the graph of g?

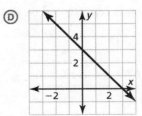

4. Condense $3 \log_6 4 - \log_6 12 + \log_6 2x$.

_____

Chapter 6 **Test Prep** (continued)

5. Which of the following functions is *even*?

   Ⓐ $f(x) - 3x^2 + 4x - 9$

   Ⓑ $g(x) = x^3 + 2x$

   Ⓒ $k(x) = xx^3 - x^2 + 7$

   Ⓓ $h(x) = 2x^4 - 4x^2 + 7x - 9$

6. What is the inverse of $f(x) = -27x^3$?

   Ⓐ $g(x) = -3\sqrt[3]{x}$

   Ⓑ $g(x) = -\frac{1}{3}\sqrt[3]{x}$

   Ⓒ $g(x) = -\sqrt[3]{3x}$

   Ⓓ $g(x) = -\sqrt[3]{\frac{1}{3}x}$

7. Select all of the following points that are solutions of the system.

   $y + x^2 \le 2$
   $y - x^2 + 6 > 2x$

   Ⓐ $(0, -2)$

   Ⓑ $(2, 4)$

   Ⓒ $(-4, 2)$

   Ⓓ $(-1, -3)$

   Ⓔ $(1, -1)$

   Ⓕ $(3, -7)$

8. Which type of function is represented by the table?

x	−6	−5	−4	−3	−2	−1
y	1458	486	162	54	18	6

   Ⓐ linear

   Ⓑ quadratic

   Ⓒ cubic

   Ⓓ exponential

Chapter 6 Test Prep (continued)

9. Use $\log_2 5 \approx 2.3219$ and $\log_2 7 \approx 2.8074$ to evaluate $\log_2 35$.

$\log_2 35 \approx$

10. You deposit $300 into an account that earns 6% annual interest compounded continuously. How much money is in the account after 5 years?

$

11. A factory is producing a mirror in the shape of a parabola to be used in searchlights. A drawing of the mirror is shown. The light from the searchlight is located at the focus of the parabola, and will shine through at the given vertex of the mirror. Find an equation that represents the parabolic mirror.

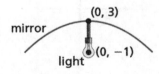

12. Select all the of the functions that represent exponential growth.

Ⓐ $f(x) = (0.99)^x$

Ⓑ $g(x) = \left(\dfrac{3}{2}\right)^x$

Ⓒ $m(x) = 5(3)^{5x}$

Ⓓ $b(x) = \dfrac{1}{4}\left(\dfrac{7}{3}\right)^{x/9}$

Ⓔ $k(x) = 12\left(\dfrac{2}{5}\right)^{2x}$

Ⓕ $h(x) = 0.2(1.1)^{x/4}$

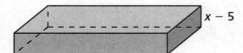

Chapter 6 **Test Prep** (continued)

13. The volume of the rectangular prism shown is given by $V = x^3 - 7x^2 + 7x + 15$. Which polynomial represents the area of the base of the pyramid?

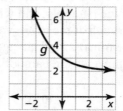

Ⓐ $-2 + -3x^2 - x$

Ⓑ $x^2 + 2x + 3$

Ⓒ $-2x + 3 - x^2$

Ⓓ $-3 + x^2 - 2x$

14. Which of the following correctly orders the logarithms $\log_3 90$, $\log_7 47$, $\log_9 85$, and $\log 9014$ from least value to greatest value?

Ⓐ $\log_7 47$, $\log_9 85$, $\log_3 90$, $\log 9014$

Ⓑ $\log_7 47$, $\log_9 85$, $\log 9014$, $\log_3 90$

Ⓒ $\log_9 85$, $\log_7 47$, $\log 9014$, $\log_3 90$

Ⓓ $\log_9 85$, $\log_7 47$, $\log_3 90$, $\log 9014$

15. Which of the following correctly describes the transformation of $f(x) = \left(\frac{1}{2}\right)^{-x} - 1$ represented by g?

Ⓐ The graph of g is a reflection in the y-axis, followed by a translation 3 units up.

Ⓑ The graph of g is a reflection in the x-axis, followed by a translation 3 units up.

Ⓒ The graph of g is a reflection in the y-axis, followed by a translation 2 units up.

Ⓓ The graph of g is a reflection in the x-axis, followed by a translation 2 units up.

Name_____ Date_____

In Exercises 1–10, tell whether *x* and *y* show *direct variation*, *inverse variation*, or *neither*.

1. $\dfrac{13}{x} = y$ **2.** $\dfrac{x}{7} = y$ **3.** $x + 11 = y$ **4.** $\dfrac{y}{9x} = 1$

5. $x - 8y = 1$ **6.** $3xy = 1$ **7.** $x = \dfrac{5}{4}y$ **8.** $6xy = 0$

9.

x	1	5	8	20	50
y	5	1	0.625	0.25	0.1

10.

x	2	5	8.4	12	15
y	0.5	1.25	2.1	3	3.75

In Exercises 11–14, the variables *x* and *y* vary inversely. Use the given values to write an equation relating *x* and *y*. Then find *y* when *x* = 5.

11. $x = 2,\ y = 2$ **12.** $x = 6,\ y = 3$

13. $x = 20,\ y = \dfrac{7}{20}$ **14.** $x = \dfrac{10}{9},\ y = \dfrac{3}{2}$

15. The time t (in days) that it takes to harvest a field varies inversely with the number n of farm workers. A farmer can harvest his crop in 20 days with 7 farm workers.

   a. Make a table showing the times that it takes to harvest the field when the number of farm workers is 14, 21, 28, and 35.

   b. What happens to the time it takes to harvest the field as the number of farm workers increase?

16. Suppose y varies directly with x and y varies inversely with z. How does x vary with z? Justify your answer.

7.1 Review & Refresh

1. Divide $(x^2 - 5x - 84) \div (x + 7)$.

2. The table shows the numbers of pairs of shoes sold y (in thousands) after x weeks. What type of function can you use to model the data? Estimate the number of pairs of shoes sold in 6 weeks.

Time (weeks), x	Pairs of shoes sold, y
0	20
5	30
10	40
15	50
20	40

3. Solve $\log_6(3 - x) = \log_6(-2x)$.

4. Which properties of logarithms can you use to condense the expression $\log x + \log 2 - \log 4$?

5. Tell whether x and y show *direct variation*, *inverse variation*, or *neither*.

x	−4	−1	2	3	6
y	−6	−24	12	8	4

6. Create a scatter plot of the points $(x, \ln y)$ to determine whether an exponential model fits the data. If so, find an exponential model for the data.

x	2	4	5	7	8
y	7.9	35.0	73.5	324.2	680.8

7. Simplify $9\sqrt[3]{108} + 7\sqrt[3]{4}$.

7.1 Self-Assessment

Use the scale to rate your understanding of the learning target and the success criteria.

1 I do not understand.	**2** I can do it with help.	**3** I can do it on my own.	**4** I can teach someone else.

	Rating	Date
7.1 Inverse Variation		
Learning Target: Understand inverse variation.	1 2 3 4	
I can identify equations and data sets that show direct variation.	1 2 3 4	
I can identify equations and data sets that show inverse variation.	1 2 3 4	
I can write inverse variation equations.	1 2 3 4	
I can solve real-life problems using inverse variation functions.	1 2 3 4	

7.2 Extra Practice

In Exercises 1 and 2, graph the function. Compare the graph with the graph of $f(x) = \dfrac{1}{x}$.

1. $h(x) = \dfrac{-2}{x}$

2. $g(x) = \dfrac{0.25}{x}$

In Exercises 3 and 4, graph the function. Find the domain and range.

3. $m(x) = \dfrac{-3}{x} - 4$

4. $k(x) = \dfrac{1}{x - 3} + 5$

In Exercises 5 and 6, rewrite the function in the form $g(x) = \dfrac{a}{x - h} + k$. Graph the function. Describe the graph of g as a transformation of the graph of $f(x) = \dfrac{a}{x}$.

5. $g(x) = \dfrac{x + 2}{x - 5}$

6. $g(x) = \dfrac{2x + 8}{3x - 12}$

7. Sketch a graph of the rational function f with the given characteristics.

   - The domain of f is all real numbers except $x = -2$.

   - $f(x) \to 1$ as $x \to -\infty$ and as $x \to +\infty$.

7.2 Review & Refresh

In Exercises 1 and 2, write a function g whose graph represents the indicated transformation of the graph of f.

1. $f(x) = x$; translation 8 units up, followed by a reflection in the y-axis

2. $f(x) = |x|$; translation 5 units right, followed by a vertical stretch by a factor of 6

In Exercises 3–5, factor the polynomial completely.

3. $x^2 + 22x + 121$ 4. $x^3 - 125$

5. $3x^3 + 24x^2 + 2x + 16$

6. The number y of pictures that can be stored on a flash drive varies inversely with the average size x of a picture. A certain flash drive can store 12,800 pictures when the average size of a picture is 2.5 megabytes. Find the number of pictures that will fit on the flash drive when the average size of a picture is 3.2 megabytes.

7. Solve $5^x = 15$.

8. Rewrite $g(x) = \dfrac{x + 3}{x - 2}$ in the form $g(x) = \dfrac{a}{x - h} + k$. Graph the function. Describe the graph of g as a transformation of the graph of $f(x) = \dfrac{a}{x}$.

9. Which functions do *not* have a domain of all real numbers?

$f(x) = (x + 3)^4$ $g(x) = \sqrt[4]{x + 3}$

$h(x) = \sqrt[5]{x + 3}$ $p(x) = \dfrac{1}{x + 3}$

7.2 Self-Assessment

Use the scale to rate your understanding of the learning target and the success criteria.

| 1 | I do not understand. | 2 | I can do it with help. | 3 | I can do it on my own. | 4 | I can teach someone else. |

	Rating	Date
7.2 Graphing Rational Functions		
Learning Target: Describe and graph rational functions.	1 2 3 4	
I can graph rational functions.	1 2 3 4	
I can describe transformations of rational functions.	1 2 3 4	
I can explain how to find the asymptotes of a rational function from an equation.	1 2 3 4	
I can write rational functions in different forms.	1 2 3 4	

Name_____ Date _____

7.3 **Extra Practice**

In Exercises 1–4, simplify the expression, if possible.

1. $\dfrac{2x^3 - 8x^2}{6x^2}$

2. $\dfrac{5xy^3 - 2x^2y^2}{x^2y^2}$

3. $\dfrac{x^2 - 5x + 4}{x^2 - 2x + 1}$

4. $\dfrac{x^3 + 3x^2}{x^2 - 5x - 24}$

In Exercises 5–8, find the product.

5. $\dfrac{3xy}{xy^2} \bullet \dfrac{y}{2x}$

6. $\dfrac{x^2 - 2x - 3}{x^2 - 1} \bullet \dfrac{x^2 - 2x - 63}{x^2 + 4x - 21}$

7. $\dfrac{x^2 + x - 30}{x^2 - 25} \bullet \left(x^2 + 3x - 10\right)$

8. $\dfrac{x^2 - 2x}{x + 7} \bullet \dfrac{x^3 + 8}{x^3 - 4x}$

In Exercises 9–12, find the quotient.

9. $\dfrac{x + y}{7xy} \div \dfrac{4x}{y}$

10. $\dfrac{9x}{2x + 6} \div \dfrac{x^2 - 8x}{x^2 - 5x - 24}$

11. $\dfrac{3x^2 + 11x - 4}{x^3} \div \left(3x^2 - 31x + 10\right)$

12. $\dfrac{x^2 + 2x - 15}{x^2 - 3x - 40} \div \dfrac{x^2 + 8x - 9}{x^2 + x - 72}$

13. Find the expression that makes the following statement true. Assume $x \neq -9$, $x \neq -6$, and $x \neq 4$.

$$\dfrac{x + 6}{x^2 + 17x + 72} \div \dfrac{x + 6}{\boxed{}} = \dfrac{x - 4}{x + 8}$$

14. Find the ratio of the perimeter to the area of the triangle shown.

Algebra 2 **115**
Practice Workbook and Test Prep

Name _____ Date _____

7.3 Review & Refresh

1. Describe the transformation of $f(x) = x^2$ represented by g.

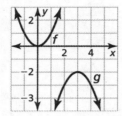

In Exercises 2 and 3, graph the function. Find the domain and range.

2. $f(x) = \dfrac{x - 2}{x + 2}$

3. $y = \dfrac{2x - 3}{-x + 4}$

In Exercises 4 and 5, the variables x and y vary inversely. Use the given values to write an equation relating x and y. Then find y when x = 8.

4. $x = 2, y = -1$

5. $x = 6, y = 4$

In Exercises 6 and 7, find the product or quotient.

6. $\dfrac{5x^2 y}{x^3 y^2} \cdot \dfrac{y^4}{10x}$

7. $\dfrac{9xy^3 z}{y^5 z^3} \div \dfrac{3x^2}{y^2 z}$

8. The number N (in millions) of motor vehicles registered in the United States from 2010 to 2017 can be modeled by the function

$$N = -0.013t^3 + 0.42t^2 + 0.9t + 251$$

where t is the number of years after 2010. Since what year are there at least 270 million motor vehicles registered?

9. Factor $2y^5 - 8y^3 - 10y$ completely.

10. Write an exponential growth function represented by the graph.

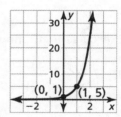

7.3 Self-Assessment

Use the scale to rate your understanding of the learning target and the success criteria.

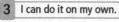

	Rating	Date
7.3 Multiplying and Dividing Rational Expressions		
Learning Target: Multiply and divide rational expressions.	1 2 3 4	
I can simplify rational expressions and identify any excluded values	1 2 3 4	
I can multiply rational expressions.	1 2 3 4	
I can divide rational expressions.	1 2 3 4	

116 Algebra 2
Practice Workbook and Test Prep

Copyright © Big Ideas Learning, LLC
All rights reserved.

Name_____ Date_____

7.4 Extra Practice

In Exercises 1–4, find the sum or difference.

1. $\dfrac{1}{x-1} - \dfrac{5}{x-1}$

2. $\dfrac{4x}{3x-5} + \dfrac{x}{3x-5}$

3. $\dfrac{6x}{x+4} + \dfrac{24}{x+4}$

4. $\dfrac{2x^2}{x-7} - \dfrac{14x}{x-7}$

In Exercises 5–7, find the least common multiple of the expressions.

5. $9x^3,\ 3x^2 - 21x$

6. $x+5,\ 2x^2 + 11x + 5$

7. $x^2 + 5x + 6,\ x^2 - 3x - 18$

In Exercises 8–13, find the sum or difference.

8. $\dfrac{3}{2x} + \dfrac{11}{5x}$

9. $\dfrac{15}{x-2} + \dfrac{3}{x+8}$

10. $\dfrac{3}{x^2 + 5x - 24} - \dfrac{10}{x-3}$

11. $\dfrac{3x}{2x+1} + \dfrac{10}{2x^2 - 5x - 3}$

12. $\dfrac{x}{x-7} - \dfrac{2}{x+1} - \dfrac{8x}{x^2 - 6x - 7}$

13. $\dfrac{x+3}{x^2 - 4} + \dfrac{x}{x+2} - \dfrac{2}{x+1}$

In Exercises 14 and 15, simplify the complex fraction.

14. $\dfrac{\dfrac{x}{10} - 3}{5 + \dfrac{1}{x}}$

15. $\dfrac{\dfrac{12}{x^2 - 7x - 44}}{\dfrac{2}{x-11} + \dfrac{1}{x+4}}$

16. Find the value of b that completes the equation.

$$\dfrac{x-60}{(x+5)(x-8)} = \dfrac{b}{(x+5)} - \dfrac{4}{(x-8)}$$

Name _____ Date _____

In Exercises 1 and 2, graph the function. Find the domain and range.

1. $g(x) = \dfrac{2}{x} - 3$ **2.** $g(x) = \dfrac{-3}{x + 1}$

5. Solve $|m + 11| = 0$.

6. Write an equation of the parabola.

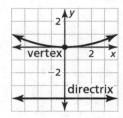

7. Graph $y > -3x^2 + 6x - 1$.

3. Tell whether x and y show *direct variation*, *inverse variation*, or *neither*.

x	7	9	11	13	15
y	28	36	44	52	60

4. An office supply store sells 80 graphing calculators each month and charges $120 per calculator. For each $6 decrease in price, the store sells 8 more calculators. How much should the store charge to maximize monthly revenue?

In Exercises 8 and 9, find the sum or difference.

8. $\dfrac{7}{10x} - \dfrac{3}{5x}$ **9.** $\dfrac{2}{x^3} + \dfrac{1}{3x}$

Use the scale to rate your understanding of the learning target and the success criteria.

1 I do not understand.	2 I can do it with help.	3 I can do it on my own.	4 I can teach someone else.

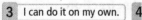

	Rating	Date
7.4 Adding and Subtracting Rational Expressions		
Learning Target: Add and subtract rational expressions.	1 2 3 4	
I can add and subtract rational expressions with like denominators.	1 2 3 4	
I can explain how to find a common denominator for rational expressions.	1 2 3 4	
I can add and subtract rational expressions with unlike denominators.	1 2 3 4	

7.5 Extra Practice

In Exercises 1–4, solve the equation by cross multiplying. Check your solution(s).

1. $\dfrac{2}{x+8} = \dfrac{5}{2x-7}$　　2. $\dfrac{x}{x+1} = \dfrac{-4}{x}$　　3. $\dfrac{x+1}{x-3} = \dfrac{x+2}{x-6}$　　4. $\dfrac{-2}{x-3} = \dfrac{x+9}{x+21}$

In Exercises 5–12, solve the equation by using the LCD. Check your solution(s).

5. $\dfrac{4}{7} - \dfrac{1}{x} = 6$

6. $\dfrac{3}{x+1} + \dfrac{4}{x+2} = \dfrac{15}{x+2}$

7. $\dfrac{12}{x+4} - \dfrac{7}{x} = \dfrac{22}{x^2+4x}$

8. $3 - \dfrac{18}{x-1} = -\dfrac{12}{x}$

9. $\dfrac{2}{x-5} + \dfrac{3}{x} = \dfrac{10}{x^2-5x}$

10. $\dfrac{x+6}{x-4} - \dfrac{30}{x^2-5x+4} = \dfrac{3}{x-1}$

11. $\dfrac{x}{x-5} + \dfrac{2}{x+2} = \dfrac{11}{x^2-3x-10}$

12. $\dfrac{x-2}{x-4} - \dfrac{2}{x-1} = \dfrac{12}{x^2-5x+4}$

13. You can complete yard work at your friend's home in 5 hours. Working together, you and your friend can complete the yard work in 3 hours.

　　a. Let t be the time (in hours) your friend takes to complete the yard work when working alone. Complete the table.
　　$\left(Hint\text{: } (\text{Work done}) = (\text{Work rate}) \times (\text{Time})\right)$

	Work rate	Time	Work done
You	$\dfrac{1 \text{ yard}}{5 \text{ hours}}$	3 hours	
Friend		3 hours	

　　b. Explain what the sum of the expressions represents in the last column. Write and solve an equation to find how long it takes your friend to complete the yard work working alone.

14. The function $c = \dfrac{0.1x + 270}{x}$ represents the average cost (in dollars) of printing x invitations on a printer. Find how many invitations you must print for the average cost per invitation to fall to \$1 by (i) solving an equation, and (ii) using the inverse of the function.

7.5 Review & Refresh

1. Evaluate $f(x) = 2x^3 - 8x^2 + 9$ when $x = -4$.

2. The linear function $c = 100t$ represents the total number of calories c burned after walking t hours.

   a. Find the domain of the function. Is the domain discrete or continuous? Explain.

   b. Graph the function using its domain.

3. Find the sum $\dfrac{x - 4}{x - 3} + \dfrac{3x + 12}{x^2 - 9x + 18}$.

4. Let $f(x) = \sqrt{x - 2}$ and $g(x) = 2x^2 + 7$. Find $f(g(-3))$ and $g(f(9))$.

In Exercises 5–8, match the function with its graph. Explain your reasoning.

5. $g(x) = \dfrac{2}{x}$

6. $g(x) = \dfrac{-2}{x} + 1$

7. $g(x) = \dfrac{-2}{x + 1} + 1$

8. $g(x) = \dfrac{-2}{x - 1}$

A. 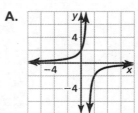   B.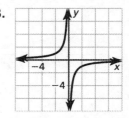

C. 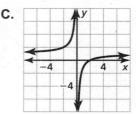   D.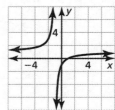

9. Solve $\dfrac{x}{x^2 - 3x} + \dfrac{1}{x - 3} = \dfrac{2x + 3}{x - 3}$. Check your solution.

7.5 Self-Assessment

Use the scale to rate your understanding of the learning target and the success criteria.

| 1 I do not understand. | 2 I can do it with help. | 3 I can do it on my own. | 4 I can teach someone else. |

	Rating	Date
7.5 Solving Rational Equations		
Learning Target: Solve rational equations.	1 2 3 4	
I can solve rational equations by cross multiplying and by using least common denominators.	1 2 3 4	
I can identify extraneous solutions of rational equations.	1 2 3 4	
I can solve real-life problems using inverses of rational functions.	1 2 3 4	

Name_____ Date_____

Chapter Self-Assessment

Use the scale to rate your understanding of the learning target and the success criteria.

	Rating	Date
Chapter 7 Rational Functions		
Learning Target: Understand rational functions.	1 2 3 4	
I can determine whether an equation represents direct variation or inverse variation.	1 2 3 4	
I can graph rational functions.	1 2 3 4	
I can add, subtract, multiply, and divide rational expressions.	1 2 3 4	
I can solve rational equations.	1 2 3 4	
7.1 Inverse Variation		
Learning Target: Understand inverse variation.	1 2 3 4	
I can identify equations and data sets that show direct variation.	1 2 3 4	
I can identify equations and data sets that show inverse variation.	1 2 3 4	
I can write inverse variation equations.	1 2 3 4	
I can solve real-life problems using inverse variation functions.	1 2 3 4	
7.2 Graphing Rational Functions		
Learning Target: Describe and graph rational functions.	1 2 3 4	
I can graph rational functions.	1 2 3 4	
I can describe transformations of rational functions.	1 2 3 4	
I can explain how to find the asymptotes of a rational function from an equation.	1 2 3 4	
I can write rational functions in different forms	1 2 3 4	
7.3 Multiplying and Dividing Rational Expressions		
Learning Target: Multiply and divide rational expressions.	1 2 3 4	
I can simplify rational expressions and identify any excluded values	1 2 3 4	
I can multiply rational expressions.	1 2 3 4	
I can divide rational expressions.	1 2 3 4	

Chapter 7 Chapter Self-Assessment (continued)

	Rating	Date
7.4 Adding and Subtracting Rational Expressions		
Learning Target: Add and subtract rational expressions.	1 2 3 4	
I can add and subtract rational expressions with like denominators.	1 2 3 4	
I can explain how to find a common denominator for rational expressions.	1 2 3 4	
I can add and subtract rational expressions with unlike denominators.	1 2 3 4	
7.5 Solving Rational Equations		
Learning Target: Solve rational equations.	1 2 3 4	
I can solve rational equations by cross multiplying and by using least common denominators.	1 2 3 4	
I can identify extraneous solutions of rational equations.	1 2 3 4	
I can solve real-life problems using inverses of rational functions.	1 2 3 4	

Name_____ Date _____

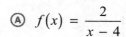
1. Which of the following functions is shown in the graph?

   Ⓐ $f(x) = \dfrac{2}{x-4}$

   Ⓑ $f(x) = \dfrac{2}{x+4}$

   Ⓒ $f(x) = \dfrac{-2}{x-4}$

   Ⓓ $f(x) = \dfrac{-2}{x+4}$

   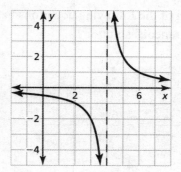

2. Find $(3x - 2)^3$.

   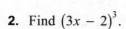

3. What type of function can you use to model the data?

Time (years), x	1	2	3	4
Sales (millions), y	1.75	2.5	3.25	4

   Ⓐ absolute value

   Ⓑ constant

   Ⓒ linear

   Ⓓ quadratic

4. Select all of the equations where x and y show direct variation.

   Ⓐ $y = x - 2$

   Ⓑ $\dfrac{3}{4}x = y$

   Ⓒ $xy = 0.3$

   Ⓓ $y = 10x$

   Ⓔ $\dfrac{y}{x} = 1.8$

5. What is the inverse of $y = e^{2x} - 1$?

   Ⓐ $y = \frac{1}{2}\ln(x + 1)$

   Ⓑ $y = \ln(2x) - 1$

   Ⓒ $y = \ln(x + 1)$

   Ⓓ $y = \ln(2x)$

Chapter 7 **Test Prep** (continued)

6. Which of the following equations has an extraneous solution?

   Ⓐ $\dfrac{x}{2x + 1} = \dfrac{2x}{x + 2}$

   Ⓑ $\dfrac{x}{x + 3} = \dfrac{6}{x - 3} + \dfrac{x^2}{x^2 - 9}$

   Ⓒ $\dfrac{5}{x - 3} + \dfrac{4}{x} = \dfrac{3}{x - 3}$

   Ⓓ $\dfrac{4x^2}{x^2 - 4} - \dfrac{2x}{x - 2} = \dfrac{1}{x + 2}$

7. What is the solution of $6\sqrt{x - 2} + 4 = 28$?

   $x =$

8. Which of the following is *not* true about the function $f(x) = -x^2 - 2x + 3$?

   Ⓐ The vertex of the function is $(-1, 4)$.

   Ⓑ The range of the function is $y \le 4$.

   Ⓒ The axis of symmetry is $x = -1$.

   Ⓓ The function is decreasing when $x < -1$ and increasing when $x > -1$.

9. Let $g(x) = \dfrac{2x + 12}{x + 3}$. Which of the following correctly describes the graph of g as a transformation of the graph of $f(x) = \dfrac{a}{x}$?

   Ⓐ The graph of g is a translation 3 units left and 2 units down of the graph of f.

   Ⓑ The graph of g is a translation 3 units right and 2 units down of the graph of f.

   Ⓒ The graph of g is a translation 3 units left and 2 units up of the graph of f.

   Ⓓ The graph of g is a translation 3 units right and 2 units up of the graph of f.

Chapter 7 Test Prep (continued)

10. For what value of k is $3(b-5)$, $a \neq 0$, $b \neq -7$ the simplified

    form of $\dfrac{b^2 + 2b - 35}{2a^2} \cdot \dfrac{6a^2}{b + k}$?

    $k =$

11. The difference of two complex numbers is $-10i$. The product of the numbers is 34. What is the sum of the numbers?

    Ⓐ $15i$

    Ⓑ 6

    Ⓒ $10i$

    Ⓓ 0

12. The graph of a rational function of the form

    $f(x) = \dfrac{1}{x - h} + k$ has asymptotes that intersect

    in the third quadrant. Which of the following are possible values of h and k? Select all that apply.

    Ⓐ $h = 2, k = -4$

    Ⓑ $h = -1, k = 3$

    Ⓒ $h = -7, k = -9$

    Ⓓ $h = 10, k = 8$

    Ⓔ $h = -5, k = -3$

    Ⓕ $h = 12, k = -15$

13. The radioactive isotope argon-37 has a daily decay rate of 2%. After 2 weeks, there are 60.3 grams of argon-37 remaining. About how many grams were initially there?

    Ⓐ 3.7 g

    Ⓑ 62.8 g

    Ⓒ 80.0 g

    Ⓓ 1371.1 g

Chapter 7 Test Prep (continued)

14. Let $p = 10$, $q = 7$, and $r = -4$. The variable p varies inversely with the sum of q and r. Write an equation that relates p, q, and r.

_____

15. The table shows the outputs of the two functions f and g. Which of the following is *not* true?

x	1	2	3	4	5
f(x)	−5	−1	0	3	10
g(x)	−1	−5	−8	−10	−15

  Ⓐ $(fg)(4) = -30$

  Ⓑ $(f + g)(5) = -5$

  Ⓒ $\left(\dfrac{g}{f}\right)(2) = 5$

  Ⓓ $(g - f)(1) = -4$

16. A cab driver drives from the airport to a passenger's home at an average speed of 60 miles per hour. After the pickup, the cab driver returns with the passenger along the same route to the airport at an average speed of 45 miles per hour. The round trip takes 2.1 hours. What was the driver's average speed throughout the entire trip?

  Ⓐ about 25.71 miles per hour

  Ⓑ about 51.43 miles per hour

  Ⓒ about 52.5 miles per hour

  Ⓓ 54 miles per hour

17. What value of b completes the equation?

$$\dfrac{-2x + 6}{(x - 4)(x - 6)} = \dfrac{1}{x - 4} - \dfrac{b}{x - 6}$$

$b =$

8.1 Extra Practice

In Exercises 1 and 2, find the number of possible outcomes in the sample space. Then list the possible outcomes.

1. A stack of cards contains the thirteen clubs from a standard deck of cards. You pick a card from the stack and flip two coins.

2. You spin a spinner with 5 equal sections (one blue, one green, one red, one yellow, and one purple) and roll a die.

3. There are two bags, each containing 10 tiles numbered 1 through 10. When one tile is chosen from each bag, there are 100 possible outcomes. Find the probability that (a) the sum of the two numbers is *not* 10 and (b) the product of the numbers is greater than 10.

4. You throw a dart at the board shown. Your dart is equally likely to hit any point inside the square board. What is the probability your dart lands in the black circle?

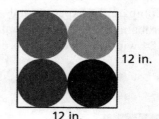

12 in.

12 in.

5. The sections of a spinner are numbered 1 through 12. Each section of the spinner has the same area. You spin the spinner 180 times. The table shows the results. For which number is the experimental probability of stopping on the number the same as the theoretical probability?

Spinner Results											
1	2	3	4	5	6	7	8	9	10	11	12
13	21	22	20	11	8	14	9	15	12	18	17

6. A manufacturer measures the length of 1500 nails and finds 100 of them to be too short. Predict the number of short nails in a box containing 2400 nails. Explain your reasoning.

Name _____ Date _____

In Exercises 1 and 2, simplify the expression.

1. $e^{\ln x}$

2. $\log_5 125^{-4x}$

3. Describe the transformation from the graph of $f(x) = x^3$ represented by $g(x) = (x - 2)^3 + 1$. Then graph each function.

4. A spinner is divided into sections with the same area. You spin the spinner 30 times. It stops on a multiple of 4 eighteen times. Compare the experimental probability of spinning a multiple of 4 with the theoretical probability.

In Exercises 5–8, perform the indicated operation.

5. $\dfrac{2x}{5y} \div \dfrac{3x}{10y}$

6. $\dfrac{2}{x - 3} + \dfrac{6x}{x - 2}$

7. $\dfrac{9}{2x^2} - \dfrac{1}{x^2 - 1}$

8. $\dfrac{x + 6}{x^2 - 2x - 24} \cdot (x^2 + x - 12)$

9. You want to order frozen yogurt from one of two shops. The table shows the total costs of a frozen yogurt with different numbers of toppings at Shop A. The total cost y (in dollars) of a frozen yogurt with x toppings at Shop B is represented by the equation $y = 0.5x + 6$. Which shop charges less per topping? How many toppings must you order for the total costs to be the same.

Shop A	
Number of toppings, x	Total cost, y
1	5.75
2	6.50
3	7.25
4	8.00

Use the scale to rate your understanding of the learning target and the success criteria.

| 1 | I do not understand. | 2 | I can do it with help. | 3 | I can do it on my own. | 4 | I can teach someone else. |

	Rating	Date
8.1 Sample Spaces and Probability		
Learning Target: Find sample spaces and probabilities of events.	1 2 3 4	
I can list the possible outcomes in a sample space.	1 2 3 4	
I can find theoretical probabilities.	1 2 3 4	
I can find experimental probabilities.	1 2 3 4	

8.2 Extra Practice

1. Complete the two-way table.

		Arrival		
		Tardy	On Time	Total
Method	Walk	22		
	City Bus			60
	Total		58	130

2. A survey was taken of 100 families with one child and 86 families with two or more children to determine whether they were saving for college. Of those, 94 of the families with one child and 60 of the families with two or more children were saving for college. Organize these results in a two-way table. Then find and interpret the marginal frequencies.

3. In a survey, 214 ninth graders played video games every day of the week and 22 ninth graders did not play video games every day of the week. Of those that played every day of the week, 36 had trouble sleeping at night. Of those that did not play every day of the week, 7 had trouble sleeping at night. Make a two-way table that shows the joint and marginal relative frequencies. Interpret one of the joint relative frequencies and one of the marginal relative frequencies.

4. Use the survey results from Exercise 2 to make a two-way table that shows the conditional relative frequencies based on (a) the row totals and (b) the column totals. Interpret one of the conditional relative frequencies in each table.

8.2 Review & Refresh

1. Determine whether the inverse of $f(x) = \dfrac{1}{2x^3} - 4$ is a function. Then find the inverse.

2. A survey finds that 18 students studied for a quiz and 9 students did not study for the quiz. Of those that studied, 16 passed the quiz. Of those who did not study, 4 passed the quiz. Make a two-way table that shows the conditional relative frequencies based on the studying totals. Then interpret one of the conditional relative frequencies.

3. Simplify $\dfrac{\dfrac{2}{x+4}}{\dfrac{4}{x+4} - \dfrac{1}{x}}$.

4. When two six-sided dice are rolled, there are 36 possible outcomes. Find the probability that the sum is *not* 4.

5. Write a rule for *g*.

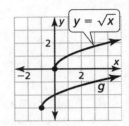

6. Tell whether $y = 3e^{x/2}$ represents *exponential growth*, or *exponential decay*. Then graph the function.

7. Expand $\log_2 \dfrac{x^2}{3}$.

8. Factor $a^3 + a^2 - 25a - 25$ completely.

8.2 Self-Assessment

Use the scale to rate your understanding of the learning target and the success criteria.

| 1 I do not understand. | 2 I can do it with help. | 3 I can do it on my own. | 4 I can teach someone else. |

	Rating	Date
8.2 Two-Way Tables and Probability		
Learning Target: Use two-way tables to represent data and find probabilities.	1 2 3 4	
I can make two-way tables.	1 2 3 4	
I can find and interpret relative frequencies and conditional relative frequencies.	1 2 3 4	
I can use conditional relative frequencies to find probabilities.	1 2 3 4	

Name _____ Date _____

1. You have three $5 bills and four $10 bills in your wallet. You randomly select two different dollar bills from your wallet. Find the probability that you select a $5 bill second given that you randomly selected a $10 bill first.

2. The two-way table shows the number of dogs and cats at three local animal shelters. Find the probability of each.

		Shelter		
		A	B	C
Animal	Dog	10	18	12
	Cat	24	20	35

    a. $P(\text{Shelter A} \mid \text{dog})$

    b. $P(\text{cat} \mid \text{Shelter B})$

3. Find the probability in Exercise 2(a) using the formula for conditional probability.

4. At a farmer's market, 75% of customers buy produce, 6% of customers buy produce and meat, and 1% of customers buy produce and flowers.

    a. What is the probability that a customer who buys produce also buys meat?

    b. What is the probability that a customer who buys produce also buys flowers?

5. You want to find the quickest route to work. You map out three routes. Before work, you randomly select a route and record whether you were late or on time. The table shows your findings. Assuming you leave at the same time each morning, which route should you use? Explain.

Route	On Time	Late
A	卌 卌 卌	III
B	卌 卌 III	IIII
C	卌 卌 卌 I	卌

6. In a survey, 62% of respondents have a tablet, 30% have a laptop, and 12% of the respondents who have a laptop also have a tablet.

    a. What is the probability that a person from the survey has both a laptop and tablet?

    b. What is the probability that a person from the survey who has a tablet also has a laptop?

8.3 Review & Refresh

1. Solve $\frac{7}{10}x - 0.2x = 3.5$.

2. Use the data to create a two-way table that shows the joint and marginal relative frequencies.

		Commercial		
		Viewed	Not Viewed	Total
Buy	Yes	42	10	52
	No	37	36	73
	Total	79	46	125

3. Let $f(x) = 8x - 4x^2 + 5$ and $g(x) = 3x^2$. Find $(f + g)(x)$ and $(f - g)(x)$ and state the domain of each. The $f + g$ and $f - g$ when $x = -1$.

4. Find $(x^2 - 2x + 3)(x^2 + 4x - 6)$.

5. Find the zeros of
$$f(x) = 2x^3 + 3x^2 - 5x - 6.$$
Then sketch a graph of the function.

6. The two-way table shows the number of defective and non-defective parts in two buildings.

		Building	
		A	B
Part Type	Defective	8	4
	Non-defective	53	48

a. $P(\text{Building A} \mid \text{defective})$

b. $P(\text{non-defective} \mid \text{Building B})$

8.3 Self-Assessment

Use the scale to rate your understanding of the learning target and the success criteria.

1	I do not understand.	2	I can do it with help.	3	I can do it on my own.	4	I can teach someone else.

	Rating	Date
8.3 Conditional Probability		
Learning Target: Find and use conditional probabilities.	1 2 3 4	
I can explain the meaning of conditional probability.	1 2 3 4	
I can find conditional probabilities.	1 2 3 4	
I can make decisions using probabilities.	1 2 3 4	

Name_____ Date_____

8.4 Extra Practice

1. You have three white golf balls and two yellow golf balls in a bag. You randomly select one golf ball to hit now and another golf ball to place in your pocket. Use a sample space to determine whether randomly selecting a white golf ball first and then a white golf ball second are independent events.

2. You roll a six-sided die two times. Use a conditional probability to determine whether getting a 1 each time are independent events.

3. A principal surveys a random sample of high school students in three grades. The survey asks whether students plan to attend the homecoming football game. The results, given as joint relative frequencies, are shown in the two-way table. Determine whether attending the game and being a junior are independent events.

		Grade		
		Sophomore	Junior	Senior
Response	Yes	0.223	0.251	0.342
	No	0.033	0.102	0.049

4. A spinner is divided into equal parts. Find the probability you get a 8 on your first spin and a number less than 6 on your second spin.

5. A music streaming queue shows 16 R&B songs and 12 pop songs. You randomly choose two songs to listen to. Find the probability that both events A and B will occur.

   Event A: The first song is a pop song.

   Event B: The second song is a R&B song.

6. You randomly select three cards from a standard deck of 52 playing cards. What is the probability that all three cards are hearts when (a) you replace each card before selecting the next card, and (b) you do not replace each card before selecting the next card?

8.4 Review & Refresh

In Exercises 1–3, solve the equation.

1. $3x^2 - 26 = 34$ 2. $2(16)^{5x} = 8$

3. $\log_7 x + \log_7(6x - 1) = 1$

4. You draw two cards from a standard deck of 52 playing cards. Each card is replaced after it is drawn. Find the probability you will draw a black card on your first draw and a diamond on your second draw.

5. A survey asks 52 males and 66 females whether they are vegetarian. Complete the two-way table. Then interpret the marginal frequencies.

		Vegetarian		
		Yes	No	Total
Gender	Male	11		
	Female		53	
	Total			

6. Simplify $\sqrt{28} - 3\sqrt{63}$.

7. Tell whether x and y show *direct variation*, *inverse variation*, or *neither*.

x	1	2	3	4
y	2.5	5	7.5	10

8. Graph $y = -(x - 4)^2 + 3$. Label the vertex and axis of symmetry.

9. Let $P(A) = 0.32$, $P(B) = 0.6$, and $P(A \text{ and } B) = 0.24$. Find $P(B \mid A)$ and $P(A \mid B)$.

10. You randomly draw a marble out of a bag containing 12 red marbles, 3 white marbles, and 5 blue marbles. Find the probability of drawing a marble that is *not* red.

8.4 Self-Assessment

Use the scale to rate your understanding of the learning target and the success criteria.

| 1 | I do not understand. | 2 | I can do it with help. | 3 | I can do it on my own. | 4 | I can teach someone else. |

	Rating	Date
8.4 Independent and Dependent Events		
Learning Target: Understand and find probabilities of independent and dependent events.	1 2 3 4	
I can explain how independent events and dependent events are different.	1 2 3 4	
I can determine whether events are independent.	1 2 3 4	
I can find probabilities of independent and dependent events.	1 2 3 4	

8.5 Extra Practice

In Exercises 1 and 2, events *A* and *B* are disjoint. Find *P(A or B)*.

1. $P(A) = 0.3, P(B) = 0.55$

2. $P(A) = \frac{2}{3}, P(B) = \frac{1}{6}$

In Exercises 3–6, a ticket is randomly chosen from a bag. The bag contains tickets numbered 1 to 16. Find the probability of the event.

3. choosing an odd number *or* a multiple of 4

4. choosing an even number *or* a factor of 25

5. choosing a number less than or equal to 10 *or* a multiple of 3

6. choosing a number greater than 3 *or* a perfect square

7. You survey 135 students. Of the students in the survey, 81 have a movie streaming subscription, 54 have a music streaming subscription, and 26 have both a movie steaming subscription and a music streaming subscription. What is the probability that a student in the survey has a movie streaming subscription *or* a music streaming subscription?

8. Out of 120 student parents, 90 of them can chaperone the homecoming dance or the prom. There are 40 parents who can chaperone the homecoming dance and 65 parents who can chaperone the prom. What is the probability that a randomly selected parent can chaperone both the homecoming dance *and* the prom?

9. A football team scores a touchdown first 75% of the time when they start with the ball. The team does not score first 51% of the time when their opponent starts with the ball. The team who gets the ball first is determined by a coin toss. What is the probability that the team scores a touchdown first?

Name _____ Date _____

8.5 Review & Refresh

1. Write $y = 2x^2 - 16x + 35$ in vertex form. Then identify the vertex.

2. A bag contains 6 winning tickets and 40 losing tickets. You randomly draw one ticket from the bag, set it aside, and then randomly draw another ticket from the bag. Find the probability you select 2 winning tickets.

3. Use the graph to solve $\log_3(x + 1) = 2$.

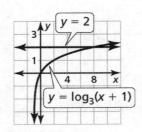

4. A group of people want to equally share the cost of renting a house for vacation. The cost per person c (in dollars) varies inversely with the number n of people sharing the cost. When 6 people share the cost, the cost per person is $83. What is the cost per person when 8 people share the cost?

5. Let $P(A) = 0.15$, $P(B) = 0.37$, and $P(A \text{ and } B) = 0.03$. Find $P(A \text{ or } B)$.

6. A teacher asks students to vote on whether they want to play dodgeball or kickball. The results are shown in the two-way table. Make a two-way table that shows the joint and marginal relative frequencies. Then interpret one of the joint relative frequencies and one of the marginal relative frequencies.

		Vote	
		Dodgeball	**Kickball**
Gender	**Male**	8	4
	Female	6	5

8.5 Self-Assessment

Use the scale to rate your understanding of the learning target and the success criteria.

1	I do not understand.	2	I can do it with help.	3	I can do it on my own.	4	I can teach someone else.

	Rating	Date
8.5 Probability of Disjoint and Overlapping Events		
Learning Target: Find probabilities of disjoint and overlapping events.	1 2 3 4	
I can explain how disjoint events and overlapping events are different.	1 2 3 4	
I can find probabilities of disjoint events.	1 2 3 4	
I can find probabilities of overlapping events.	1 2 3 4	
I can solve real-life problems using more than one probability rule.	1 2 3 4	

136 Algebra 2
Practice Workbook and Test Prep

8.6 Extra Practice

In Exercises 1 and 2, find the number of ways you can arrange (a) all of the numbers and (b) 3 of the numbers in the given amount.

1. $2,564,783

2. $4,128,675,309

3. Your rock band has nine songs recorded but you only want to put five of them on your demo CD to hand out to publishers. How many possible ways could the five songs be ordered on your demo CD?

4. A witness at the scene of a hit-and-run accident saw that the car that caused the accident had a license plate with only the letters I, R, L, T, O, and A. Find the probability that the license plate starts with a T and ends with an R.

In Exercises 5 and 6, count the possible combinations of *r* letters chosen from the given list.

5. G, H, I, J, K; $r = 2$

6. P, Q, R, S, T, U, V, W; $r = 4$

7. How many possible combinations of three colors can be chosen from the seven colors of the rainbow?

8. Use the Binomial Theorem to write the binomial expansion of $\left(2x^4 + y^3\right)^3$.

9. You are ordering a smoothie with 3 fruits and 2 vegetables. The menu shows the possible choices. How many different smoothies are possible?

10. The organizer of a gift exchange asks each of 5 people to bring 1 gift card from a list of 8 gift cards. Assuming each person randomly chooses a gift card, what is the probability that at least 2 of the 5 people bring the same gift card?

8.6   Review & Refresh

1. Graph $f(x) = |x + 3| - 2$. Then describe the transformations from the graph of $f(x) = |x|$ to the graph of the function.

2. Use the Binomial Theorem to write the binomial expansion of $(3x + y)^3$.

3. You are taking a quiz and randomly guessing the answers to three true-false questions. Use a sample space to determine whether guessing the incorrect answer to Question 1 and guessing the correct answer to Question 2 are independent events.

4. Events A and B are dependent. Suppose $P(A \text{ and } B) = 0.07$ and $P(A) = 0.35$. Find $P(B \mid A)$.

5. Graph $g(x) = (3x)^{1/2} - 1$. Find the domain and range of the function.

6. Determine the type of function represented by the table. Explain your reasoning.

x	-2	-1	0	1	2
y	1	6	36	216	1296

7. Solve the equation $\frac{1}{2}x^2 = 6 - x^2$ by graphing.

8. Events A and B are disjoint. Find $P(A \text{ or } B)$ when $P(A) = 0.25$ and $P(B) = 0.75$.

8.6   Self-Assessment

Use the scale to rate your understanding of the learning target and the success criteria.

1	I do not understand.	2	I can do it with help.	3	I can do it on my own.	4	I can teach someone else.

	Rating	Date
8.6 Permutations and Combinations		
Learning Target: Count permutations and combinations.	1 2 3 4	
I can explain the difference between permutations and combinations.	1 2 3 4	
I can find numbers of permutations and combinations.	1 2 3 4	
I can find probabilities using permutations and combinations.	1 2 3 4	

8.7 Extra Practice

In Exercises 1 and 2, make a table and draw a histogram showing the probability distribution for the random variable.

1. d = the number on a rubber duck randomly chosen from a pool that contains 8 ducks labeled "1," 4 ducks labeled "2," 5 ducks labeled "3," and 3 ducks labeled "4."

2. x = the product when two six-sided dice are rolled.

3. Use the probability distribution to determine (a) the number that is most likely to be spun on a spinner, and (b) the probability of spinning a perfect square.

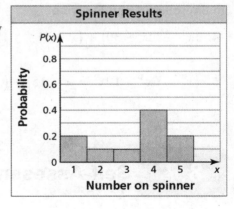

4. According to a survey, 78% of women in a city watch professional football. You ask 4 randomly chosen women from the city whether they watch professional football.

   a. Draw a histogram of the binomial distribution for your survey.

   b. What is the most likely outcome of the survey?

   c. What is the probability that at most one woman watches professional football?

8.7 Review & Refresh

1. Use the probability distribution below to determine the most likely number drawn from a bag that contains tickets numbered 1 through 5.

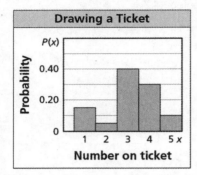

In Exercises 2 and 3, count the possible combinations of *r* letters chosen from the given list.

2. A, B, C, D, E; $r = 2$

3. L, M, N, O, P, Q; $r = 3$

In Exercises 4 and 5, divide.

4. $\left(x^2 + 11x + 30\right) \div (x + 5)$

5. $\left(x^4 - 6x^3 + 10x^2 + x - 15\right) \div (x - 3)$

6. Let the graph of g be a translation 6 units left, followed by a horizontal stretch by a factor of 3 of the graph of $f(x) = x^2 + x + 2$. Write a rule for g.

7. You collect data about a food truck competition. Of the 12 food trucks in the competition, 3 receive a trophy, 8 receive a plaque, and 2 receive a trophy and a plaque. What is the probability that a food truck in the competition receives a trophy *or* a plaque?

8. A box contains five almond granola bars, two honey granola bars, and three chocolate granola bars. You randomly select a granola bar to eat now. Then you randomly select another granola bar for your lunch.

   Event *A*: You select an almond granola bar first.
   Event *B*: You select a honey granola bar second.

   Tell whether the events are independent or dependent. Explain your reasoning.

8.7 Self-Assessment

Use the scale to rate your understanding of the learning target and the success criteria.

| 1 I do not understand. | 2 I can do it with help. | 3 I can do it on my own. | 4 I can teach someone else. |

	Rating	Date
8.7 Binomial Distribution		
Learning Target: Understand binomial distributions.	1 2 3 4	
I can explain the meaning of a probability distribution.	1 2 3 4	
I can construct and interpret probability distributions.	1 2 3 4	
I can find probabilities using binomial distributions.	1 2 3 4	

Chapter 8 — Chapter Self-Assessment

Use the scale to rate your understanding of the learning target and the success criteria.

1 I do not understand. **2** I can do it with help. **3** I can do it on my own. **4** I can teach someone else.

	Rating	Date
Chapter 8 Probability		
Learning Target: Understand probability.	1 2 3 4	
I can define theoretical and experimental probability.	1 2 3 4	
I can use two-way tables to find probabilities.	1 2 3 4	
I can compare independent and dependent events.	1 2 3 4	
I can construct and interpret probability and binomial distributions.	1 2 3 4	
8.1 Sample Spaces and Probability		
Learning Target: Find sample spaces and probabilities of events.	1 2 3 4	
I can list the possible outcomes in a sample space.	1 2 3 4	
I can find theoretical probabilities.	1 2 3 4	
I can find experimental probabilities.	1 2 3 4	
8.2 Two-Way Tables and Probability		
Learning Target: Use two-way tables to represent data and find probabilities.	1 2 3 4	
I can make two-way tables.	1 2 3 4	
I can find and interpret relative frequencies and conditional relative frequencies.	1 2 3 4	
I can use conditional relative frequencies to find probabilities.	1 2 3 4	
8.3 Conditional Probability		
Learning Target: Find and use conditional probabilities.	1 2 3 4	
I can explain the meaning of conditional probability.	1 2 3 4	
I can find conditional probabilities.	1 2 3 4	
I can make decisions using probabilities.	1 2 3 4	

Chapter Self-Assessment (continued)

	Rating	Date
8.4 Independent and Dependent Events		
Learning Target: Understand and find probabilities of independent and dependent events.	1 2 3 4	
I can explain how independent events and dependent events are different.	1 2 3 4	
I can determine whether events are independent.	1 2 3 4	
I can find probabilities of independent and dependent events.	1 2 3 4	
8.5 Probability of Disjoint and Overlapping Events		
Learning Target: Find probabilities of disjoint and overlapping events.	1 2 3 4	
I can explain how disjoint events and overlapping events are different.	1 2 3 4	
I can find probabilities of disjoint events.	1 2 3 4	
I can find probabilities of overlapping events.	1 2 3 4	
I can solve real-life problems using more than one probability rule.	1 2 3 4	
8.6 Permutations and Combinations		
Learning Target: Count permutations and combinations.	1 2 3 4	
I can explain the difference between permutations and combinations.	1 2 3 4	
I can find numbers of permutations and combinations.	1 2 3 4	
I can find probabilities using permutations and combinations.	1 2 3 4	
8.7 Binomial Distribution		
Learning Target: Understand binomial distributions.	1 2 3 4	
I can explain the meaning of a probability distribution.	1 2 3 4	
I can construct and interpret probability distributions.	1 2 3 4	
I can find probabilities using binomial distributions.	1 2 3 4	

Chapter 8 Test Prep

1. Let $P(A) = 0.4$, $P(B) = 0.6$, and $P(A \text{ and } B) = 0.12$. What is $P(A \mid B)$?

$P(A \mid B) = $

2. Solve $3^{2x-3} = 27$.

$x = $

3. What is the quotient $\dfrac{3h^3}{7j^5} \div \dfrac{18h}{21j^3}$?

Ⓐ $\dfrac{h^2}{2j^2}, h \neq 0$

Ⓑ $\dfrac{18h^4}{49j^8}$

Ⓒ $\dfrac{h^2 j^2}{2}, h \neq 0, j \neq 0$

Ⓓ $\dfrac{j^2}{2h^2}, j \neq 0$

4. Which expression is equivalent to e^4?

Ⓐ $e^{-1} \bullet e^0 \bullet e^{-3}$

Ⓑ $e^{-6}\left(e^2\right)^8$

Ⓒ $\left(e^5\right)^{-1} e^9$

Ⓓ $e^{-7x} \bullet e^{7x-4}$

5. Events A and B are independent. $P(A) = 0.4$ and $P(A \text{ and } B) = 0.38$. Find $P(B)$.

Ⓐ $P(B) = 0.95$

Ⓑ $P(B) = 0.78$

Ⓒ $P(B) = 0.152$

Ⓓ $P(B) = 0.02$

Chapter 8 **Test Prep** (continued)

6. Use the Binomial Theorem to write the binomial expansion of $(2y - 5)^3$.

_____

7. Factor $x^3 + 10x^2 - 16x - 160$ completely.

_____

8. Use the probability distribution to answer the question. What is the probability of spinning a factor of 8?

Ⓐ 75%

Ⓑ 70%

Ⓒ 60%

Ⓓ 10%

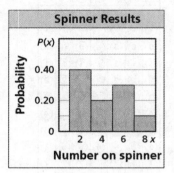

Spinner Results

9. Which of the following describes the number and type of solutions of the quadratic equation that is graphed in the coordinate plane?

Ⓐ one real solution

Ⓑ two real solutions

Ⓒ one imaginary solution

Ⓓ two imaginary solutions

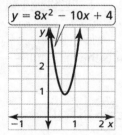

$y = 8x^2 - 10x + 4$

10. A bag contains 6 pennies, 5 nickels, 3 dimes, 5 quarters, and 2 one-dollar coins. You randomly draw a coin from the bag, set it aside, and then randomly draw another coin from the bag. What is the probability that events A and B will occur?

Event A: The first coin is quarter.   **Event B:** The second coin is quarter.

Ⓐ $\dfrac{25}{441}$

Ⓑ $\dfrac{20}{441}$

Ⓒ $\dfrac{5}{84}$

Ⓓ $\dfrac{1}{21}$

Chapter 8 Test Prep (continued)

11. A company surveys all of its employees about which benefit package they want. The two-way table shows the results. Select all the true statements about the two-way table.

		Benefit Package	
		A	**B**
Gender	**Male**	5	3
	Female	4	8

    Ⓐ The company has 20 employees.

    Ⓑ Five employees choose Package A and three employees choose Package B.

    Ⓒ The probability that a randomly selected employee from the survey chooses Package A is 45%.

    Ⓓ The probability that a randomly selected employee from the survey is male is 40%.

    Ⓔ The probability that a randomly selected employee from the survey is a female that chooses Package B is about 66.7%.

12. Out of 500 people enrolled in gym classes, 360 people take either yoga or boxing. There are 154 people who take the yoga class and 248 people who take the boxing class. What is the probability that a randomly selected person takes both the yoga class *and* the boxing class?

$P(\text{yoga and boxing}) =$

13. Select all the statements that describe the transformation of the graph of
$f(x) = x^4 + x^2 + 1$ represented by $g(x) = \frac{1}{3}(x + 7)^4 + \frac{1}{3}(x + 7)^2 + \frac{1}{3}$.

    Ⓐ a horizontal translation 7 units right

    Ⓑ a horizontal translation 7 units left

    Ⓒ a vertical shrink by a factor of $\frac{1}{3}$

    Ⓓ a horizontal stretch by a factor of 3

    Ⓔ a horizontal shrink by a factor of $\frac{1}{3}$

Chapter 8 Test Prep (continued)

14. You throw a dart at the board shown. Your dart is equally likely to hit any point inside the square board. What is the probability your dart lands in the square region that is outside the circle?

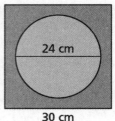

24 cm

30 cm

Ⓐ about 8.4%

Ⓑ about 49.7%

Ⓒ about 50.3%

Ⓓ about 91.6%

15. The cylinder has a volume of 628 cubic inches. What is the radius of the cylinder?

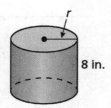

r

8 in.

Ⓐ about 5 in.

Ⓑ about 9 in.

Ⓒ about 25 in.

Ⓓ about 78.5 in.

16. Two consecutive negative odd integers have a product of 255, What is the greatest integer?

greatest integer =

17. You are ordering an omelet with 2 meats, 3 vegetables, and 1 cheese. The menu shows the possible choices. How many different omelets are possible?

Meats
• Bacon
• Chicken
• Ham
• Sausage
• Steak

Vegetables
• Broccoli
• Green pepper
• Mushroom
• Onion
• Spinach
• Tomato

Cheese
• Cheddar
• Feta
• Mozzarella

Ⓐ 33

Ⓑ 450

Ⓒ 600

Ⓓ 7200

9.1 Extra Practice

In Exercises 1–4, a normal distribution has mean μ and standard deviation σ. Find the indicated probability for a randomly selected x-value from the distribution.

1. $P(x \leq \mu - 2\sigma)$

2. $P(x \geq \mu + 3\sigma)$

3. $P(\mu - \sigma \leq x \leq \mu + 3\sigma)$

4. $P(\mu - 2\sigma \leq x \leq \mu + \sigma)$

5. The scores for a math test are normally distributed with a mean of 61 and a standard deviation of 11. The test scores range from 0 to 100.

  a. About what percent of the students taking the test have scores between 72 and 83?

  b. About what percent of the students taking the test have scores less than 50?

6. The daily high temperatures of a city are normally distributed over a year. The mean temperature is 55.2°F and the standard deviation is 6.3°F. A day is randomly chosen.

  a. What is the probability that the temperature is 45°F or cooler?

  b. What is the probability that the temperature is cooler than 32.5°F?

  c. What is the probability that the temperature is between 32.5°F and 45°F?

  d. What is the probability that the temperature is 60°F or warmer?

In Exercises 7 and 8, determine whether the histogram has a normal distribution.

7.

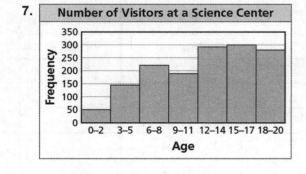

8.

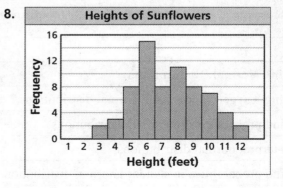

Name _____ Date _____

9.1 Review & Refresh

1. Graph $f(x) = x^3 + 4x^2 + x - 6$. Identify the x-intercepts and the points where the local maximums and local minimums occur. Determine the intervals for which the function is increasing or decreasing.

2. What percent of area under the normal curve is represented by the shaded region?

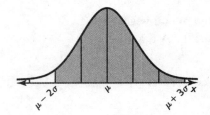

3. A card is randomly selected from a standard deck of 52 playing cards. What is the probability that it is black *or* a 3?

4. There are 40 people at a glassblowing demonstration. The artist randomly selects 2 people to participate in the demonstration. What is the probability that you and your friend are selected?

5. Evaluate $\ln 18$ using technology. Round your answer to three decimal places.

6. Let x be a random variable that represents the number on a rock that is randomly chosen from a bag that contains 6 rocks labeled "1" and 4 rocks labeled "2." Make a table and draw a histogram showing the probability distribution for x.

7. Solve the system using any method. Explain your choice of method.

   $$y = x^2 + 3x + 4$$
   $$y = 3x + 4$$

9.1 Self-Assessment

Use the scale to rate your understanding of the learning target and the success criteria.

| 1 | I do not understand. | 2 | I can do it with help. | 3 | I can do it on my own. | 4 | I can teach someone else. |

	Rating	Date
9.1 Using Normal Distributions		
Learning Target: Understand normal distributions.	1 2 3 4	
I can find probabilities in normal distributions.	1 2 3 4	
I can interpret normal distributions.	1 2 3 4	
I can find probabilities in standard normal distributions.	1 2 3 4	

Name _____ Date _____

9.2 Extra Practice

In Exercises 1 and 2, identify the population and the sample. Describe the sample.

1. To find out the consumers' responses towards a new flavor of sports drink, a company surveys 1000 athletes who drink sports drinks and finds that 726 of them like the new flavor.

2. In a school district, a survey of 1500 high school students found that 824 of them have a part-time job in the summer.

In Exercises 3–5, determine whether the numerical value is a parameter or a statistic. Explain your reasoning.

3. Eighty-two percent of the residents in one neighborhood in a town voted to approve building a bike lane through town.

4. In a science class, 25% of the students wear glasses.

5. A survey of some visitors to a museum found that 84% thought the new planetarium was very exciting.

6. You spin the spinner shown 5 times and get blue every time. You suspect the spinner favors blue. The maker of the spinner claims that the spinner does not favor any color. You use technology to simulate 200 random samples of spinning the spinner 50 times. What should you conclude when you spin the actual spinner 50 times and get blue (a) 12 times and (b) 19 times?

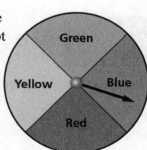

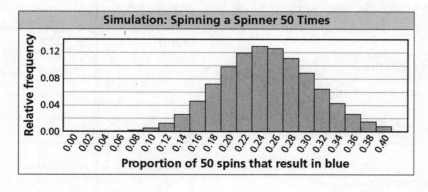

Name _____ Date _____

1. Solve $2x^2 - 12x = 8$ using any method. Explain your choice of method.

2. Determine whether the histogram has a normal distribution.

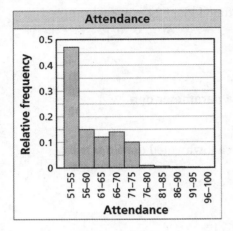

3. Identify the population and the sample. Describe the sample.

   In a city, a survey of 3257 adults ages 18 and over found that 2605 of them own a tablet.

4. Find the probability of rolling a 4 eight times in 30 rolls of a six-sided die.

In Exercises 5 and 6, evaluate the expression.

5. $_{15}P_3$

6. $_8C_5$

7. The table shows the inputs and outputs of two functions. Use the table to find each value.

x	−3	−2	−1	0	1	2
f(x)	1	0	−1	−2	−3	−4
g(x)	−1	0	1	0	−1	−2

a. $f(g(-2))$

b. $g(f(1))$

In Exercises 8 and 9, perform the operation.

8. $\dfrac{5x^2 y^3}{xy^4} \cdot \dfrac{y^2}{10x}$

9. $\dfrac{8}{x+1} - \dfrac{6}{x+1}$

9.2 Self-Assessment

Use the scale to rate your understanding of the learning target and the success criteria.

| 1 | I do not understand. | 2 | I can do it with help. | 3 | I can do it on my own. | 4 | I can teach someone else. |

	Rating	Date
9.2 Populations, Samples, and Hypotheses		
Learning Target: Use random samples and simulations to make conclusions.	1 2 3 4	
I can distinguish between populations and samples.	1 2 3 4	
I can find a sample proportion.	1 2 3 4	
I can use a simulation to test a hypothesis.	1 2 3 4	

9.3 Extra Practice

In Exercises 1–3, identify the type of sample described.

1. A restaurant owner wants to know whether the customers are satisfied with the service. Every fifth customer who exits the restaurant is surveyed.

2. An electronic manufacturer wants to know the customers' responses towards a newly released fitness tracker. Emails are sent to customers who recently purchased the device to participate in an online survey at their convenience.

3. A survey is conducted in a state to find out how many households have more than one vehicle. Households are divided into north, east, south, and west regions of the state, and a sample is randomly surveyed from each region.

In Exercises 4 and 5, identify the type of sample and explain why the sample is biased.

4. A manager of a company wants to determine whether the employees are satisfied with the lounge room. The manager surveys the employees who are in the lounge room during lunch break.

5. A news station asks its viewers to participate in an online poll about the new segment on the show.

In Exercises 6 and 7, identify the method of data collection described in the situation.

6. A researcher records whether shoppers at a grocery store buy magazines at the checkout aisles while waiting in line.

7. A meteorologist uses a computer model to track the trajectory of a hurricane.

8. Your classmate surveys people in your school by asking, "Do you think students and administrators should receive discounted tickets to school sporting events?" Explain why the question may be biased or otherwise introduce bias into the survey. Then describe a way to correct the flaw.

Name _____ Date _____

9.3   Review & Refresh

1. In a recent year, the median household income in the United States was about \$63,336. Is the median household income a parameter or a statistic? Explain your reasoning.

In Exercises 2 and 3, simplify the expression.

2. $\left(3^{2/3} \cdot 3^{1/6}\right)^6$

3. $\dfrac{\sqrt[3]{432}}{\sqrt[3]{2}}$

4. A normal distribution has a mean of 16 and a standard deviation of 3. Find the probability that a randomly selected x-value from the distribution is between 13 and 25.

5. Expand $\log_4 \dfrac{x}{3y^2}$.

6. An airline company wants to know whether its passengers are satisfied with the service. Flight attendants survey every fifth passenger during the day. What type of sample is being used?

7. Find the probability of flipping a coin 20 times and getting 3 tails.

In Exercises 8 and 9, evaluate the expression without using technology.

8. $-100^{1/2}$

9. $81^{3/4}$

10. A survey of 50 teenagers asked what genre of movie they like best. The results are shown. What is the probability that a randomly selected teenager from the survey likes drama movies best?

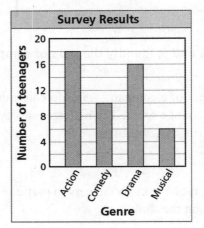

9.3   Self-Assessment

Use the scale to rate your understanding of the learning target and the success criteria.

| 1 | I do not understand. | 2 | I can do it with help. | 3 | I can do it on my own. | 4 | I can teach someone else. |

	Rating	Date
9.3 Collecting Data		
Learning Target: Describe sampling methods and recognize bias when collecting data.	1 2 3 4	
I can identify types of sampling methods in statistical studies.	1 2 3 4	
I can analyze methods of collecting data.	1 2 3 4	
I can describe bias in sampling and in survey questions.	1 2 3 4	

152 Algebra 2
Practice Workbook and Test Prep

9.4 Extra Practice

1. Determine whether the study is a randomized comparative experiment. If it is, describe the treatment, the treatment group, and the control group. If it is not, explain why not and discuss whether the conclusions drawn from the study are valid.

Baby Shows
Baby Shows Improve Language Ability
To test whether baby shows that highlight words and introduce music and art can improve language ability, parents with babies 0–24 months were given the choice of whether to let their babies watch the shows. Fifty babies who watched the shows were observed for a year, as well as 50 other babies who did not watch the shows. At the end of the year, babies who watched the shows scored higher in a language development test.

In Exercises 2 and 3, determine whether the research topic is best investigated through an experiment or an observational study. Then describe the design of the experiment or observational study.

2. A criminologist wants to know whether social factors are the cause of criminal behavior.

3. A pharmaceutical company wants to know whether a new medication for heart disease has a side effect on individuals.

4. A company wants to test the effectiveness of a new moisturizing cream designed to help improve skin complexion. Identify a potential problem, if any, with each experimental design. Then describe how you can improve it.

   a. The company randomly selects 10 individuals. Five subjects are given the new moisturizing cream and the other five are given a placebo. After 8 weeks, each subject is evaluated and it is determined that the 5 subjects who have been using the cream have improved skin complexion.

   b. The company randomly selects 5000 individuals. Half of the subjects are given the new moisturizing cream and the other half may use their own moisturizing cream or none at all. After 8 weeks, each subject is evaluated and it is determined that a significantly large number of subjects who have been using the new moisturizing cream have improved skin complexion.

9.4 Review & Refresh

1. Display the data in a dot plot. Describe the shape of the distribution.

Televisions in household			
2	4	2	5
2	1	1	2
1	3	3	2

In Exercises 4 and 5, tell whether the function represents *exponential growth* or *exponential decay*. Then graph the function.

4. $y = \left(\dfrac{4}{3}\right)^x$

5. $y = (0.8)^x$

2. A quarterback throws 3 completed passes in the first 7 throws. How many consecutive completed passes must the quarterback throw to reach a pass completion percentage of 60%?

6. You use technology to simulate rolling a six-sided die 30 times. The results are shown in the bar graph. What proportion of the 30 rolls resulted in a 4?

3. Determine whether the following research topic is best investigated through an experiment or an observational study. Then describe the design of the experiment or observational study.

   A researcher wants to know whether listening to music improves a student's ability to take a test.

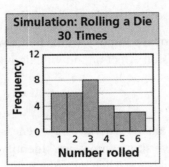

9.4 Self-Assessment

Use the scale to rate your understanding of the learning target and the success criteria.

| 1 | I do not understand. | 2 | I can do it with help. | 3 | I can do it on my own. | 4 | I can teach someone else. |

	Rating	Date
9.4 Experimental Design		
Learning Target: Describe and analyze experiments and their designs.	1 2 3 4	
I can assess the validity of an experiment's results.	1 2 3 4	
I can design an experiment or observational study.	1 2 3 4	
I can analyze experimental designs.	1 2 3 4	

9.5 Extra Practice

1. The numbers of minutes spent each day on a social networking website by a random sample of social network users between the ages of 18 and 64 are shown in the table. Estimate the population mean μ.

Number of Minutes					
175	15	190	180	45	100
210	240	190	60	102	165
253	192	102	12	180	189
193	230	300	185	190	395
186	183	200	165	195	409

2. Use the data in Exercise 1 to answer each question.

   a. Estimate the population proportion ρ of social network users between the ages of 18 and 64 who spend more than 120 minutes each day on a social networking website.

   b. Estimate the population proportion ρ of social network users between the ages of 18 and 64 who spend fewer than 60 minutes each day on a social networking website.

3. Two candidates, A and B, are running for the student council president position. The table shows the results from four surveys of randomly selected students in the school. The students are asked whether they will vote for candidate A.

Sample Size	Number of Votes for Candidate A in the Sample	Percent of Votes for Candidate A in the Sample
10	6	60%
20	11	55%
50	20	40%
150	64	42.7%

   a. Based on the results of the first two sample surveys, do you think Candidate A will win the election? Explain.

   b. Based on the results in the table, do you think Candidate A will win the election? Explain.

4. A national polling company claims that 39% of Americans rate the overall quality of the environment in the nation as "good." You survey a random sample of 50 people. What can you conclude about the accuracy of the claim that the population proportion is 0.39 when 19 people say the quality of the environment is good?

Name _____ Date _____

1. Find the inverse of $y = \ln(2x - 4)$.

In Exercises 2 and 3, determine whether the graph represents an arithmetic sequence or a geometric sequence. Then write a rule for the nth term.

2.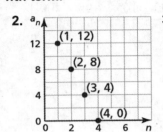

3.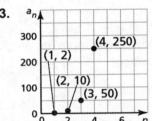

4. In a survey of 2680 people in the U.S., 60% said that their diet is somewhat healthy. Give an interval that is likely to contain the exact percent of all people in the U.S. who think their diet is somewhat healthy.

5. Find $\dfrac{x^2 + 2x}{x^2 - 6x + 5} \bullet \dfrac{x^2 - 2x - 15}{x^2 - 2x}$.

6. Determine whether the study is a randomized comparative experiment. If it is, describe the treatment, the treatment group, and the control group. If it is not, explain why not and discuss whether the conclusions drawn from the study are valid.

Type 1 Diabetes
New Drug Improves Blood Glucose
In a clinical trial, 100 Type 1 diabetic patients volunteered to take a new drug. Fifty percent of the patients received the drug and the other fifty percent received a placebo. After one year, the patients who received the drug had better blood glucose control while the placebo group experienced no significant change.

7. In the United States, a survey of 1030 adults ages 18 and over found that 278 of them have not read a book in the past year. Identify the population and the sample. Describe the sample.

Use the scale to rate your understanding of the learning target and the success criteria.

1 I do not understand.	**2** I can do it with help.	**3** I can do it on my own.	**4** I can teach someone else.

	Rating	Date
9.5 Making Inferences from Sample Surveys		
Learning Target: Use sample surveys to make conclusions about populations.	1 2 3 4	
I can estimate population parameters.	1 2 3 4	
I can analyze the accuracy of a hypothesis using simulations.	1 2 3 4	
I can find margins of error for surveys.	1 2 3 4	

Name_____ Date_____

1. A randomized comparative experiment tests whether students who are given weekly quizzes do better on the comprehensive final exam. The control group has 10 students and the treatment group, which receives weekly quizzes, has 10 students. The table shows the results.

Final Exam Scores (out of 100)										
Control Group	82	55	76	92	76	76	82	58	69	79
Treatment Group	92	90	88	73	88	63	94	81	81	77

   a. Find the experimental difference of the mean of the treatment group, $\bar{x}_{treatment}$, and the mean of the control group, $\bar{x}_{control}$.

   b. Display the data in a double dot plot.

   c. What can you conclude from parts (a) and (b)?

2. Resample the data in Exercise 1 using a simulation. Use the means of the new control and treatment groups to calculate the difference of the means.

Final Exam Scores (out of 100)										
New Control Group										
New Treatment Group										

Name _____ Date _____

1. The numbers of missed school days by a random sample of 32 students during a school year are shown in the table. Estimate the population mean μ.

Missed School Days

0	3	5	4	4	2	3	1
3	3	8	3	4	0	1	6
2	5	4	3	2	3	4	0
7	4	3	1	0	3	4	2

2. Events A and B are independent. Let $P(B) = 0.5$ and $P(A \text{ and } B) = 0.35$. Find $P(A)$.

3. Graph the function $f(x) = (x + 1)^2 - 3$. Label the vertex and axis of symmetry.

4. A randomized comparative experiment tests whether a software update to an application affects the user satisfaction scores of all application users. Greater scores indicate greater satisfaction. The control group has eight users and the treatment group, which receives the software update, has eight users. Analyze the hypothesis below. The histogram shows the results from 200 resamplings of the data.

The software update to the application has no effect on the satisfaction score.

Compare the experimental difference $\overline{x}_{treatment} - \overline{x}_{control} = 0.11$, with the resampling differences. What can you conclude about the hypothesis? Does the software update to the application improve user satisfaction?

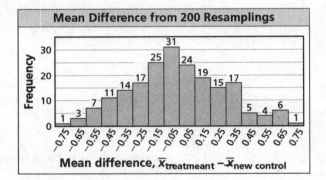

9.6 Self-Assessment

Use the scale to rate your understanding of the learning target and the success criteria.

| 1 | I do not understand. | 2 | I can do it with help. | 3 | I can do it on my own. | 4 | I can teach someone else. |

	Rating	Date
9.6 Making Inferences from Experiments		
Learning Target: Understand how to make inferences from experiments.	1 2 3 4	
I can analyze data from an experiment.	1 2 3 4	
I can explain how to resample data.	1 2 3 4	
I can use resampling to make inferences about a treatment.	1 2 3 4	

Name_____ Date _____

Chapter Self-Assessment

Use the scale to rate your understanding of the learning target and the success criteria.

	Rating	Date
Chapter 9 Data Analysis and Statistics		
Learning Target: Understand data analysis and statistics.	1 2 3 4	
I can find probabilities in normal distributions.	1 2 3 4	
I can identify populations and samples.	1 2 3 4	
I can explain different methods for collecting data.	1 2 3 4	
I can make inferences from sample surveys and experiments.	1 2 3 4	
9.1 Using Normal Distributions		
Learning Target: Understand normal distributions.	1 2 3 4	
I can find probabilities in normal distributions.	1 2 3 4	
I can interpret normal distributions.	1 2 3 4	
I can find probabilities in standard normal distributions.	1 2 3 4	
9.2 Populations, Samples, and Hypotheses		
Learning Target: Use random samples and simulations to make conclusions.	1 2 3 4	
I can distinguish between populations and samples.	1 2 3 4	
I can find a sample proportion.	1 2 3 4	
I can use a simulation to test a hypothesis.	1 2 3 4	
9.3 Collecting Data		
Learning Target: Describe sampling methods and recognize bias when collecting data.	1 2 3 4	
I can identify types of sampling methods in statistical studies.	1 2 3 4	
I can analyze methods of collecting data.	1 2 3 4	
I can describe bias in sampling and in survey questions.	1 2 3 4	

Chapter 9 Chapter Self-Assessment (continued)

	Rating				Date
9.4 Experimental Design					
Learning Target: Describe and analyze experiments and their designs.	1	2	3	4	
I can assess the validity of an experiment's results.	1	2	3	4	
I can design an experiment or observational study.	1	2	3	4	
I can analyze experimental designs.	1	2	3	4	
9.5 Making Inferences from Sample Surveys					
Learning Target: Use sample surveys to make conclusions about populations.	1	2	3	4	
I can estimate population parameters.	1	2	3	4	
I can analyze the accuracy of a hypothesis using simulations.	1	2	3	4	
I can find margins of error for surveys.	1	2	3	4	
9.6 Making Inferences from Experiments					
Learning Target: Understand how to make inferences from experiments.	1	2	3	4	
I can analyze data from an experiment.	1	2	3	4	
I can explain how to resample data.	1	2	3	4	
I can use resampling to make inferences about a treatment.	1	2	3	4	

Chapter 9 **Test Prep**

1. Which graph represents the function $f(x) = 3^{x-1}$?

Ⓐ
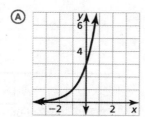

Ⓑ
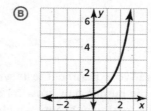

Ⓒ
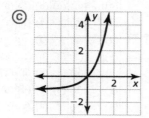

Ⓓ
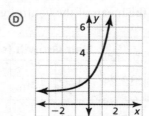

2. A normal distribution has a mean of 122 and a standard deviation of 6. What is the probability that a randomly selected x-value from the distribution is at least 116?

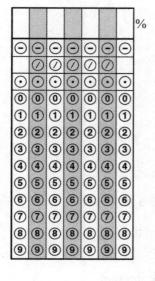

3. Which cubic function passes through the points $(-1, 0)$, $(2, 18)$, $(3, 0)$, and $(4, 0)$?

Ⓐ $h(x) = 3x^3 - 18x^2 + 15x + 36$

Ⓑ $h(x) = x^3 - 6x^2 + 5x + 12$

Ⓒ $h(x) = 3x^3 + 18x^2 + 15x - 36$

Ⓓ $h(x) = x^3 + 6x^2 + 5x - 12$

Chapter 9 **Test Prep** (continued)

4. Simplify $w\sqrt[4]{162w^3} + \sqrt[4]{32w^7}$. Assume all variables are positive.

   _____

5. A randomized comparative experiment tests whether a hair growth supplement increases the human hair growth rate. The control group has nine people and the treatment group, which receives the hair supplement, has nine people. The table below shows the results. What is the experimental difference of the mean of the treatment group, $\overline{x}_{treatment}$, and the mean of the control group, $\overline{x}_{control}$?

Hair Growth (centimeters)								
Control Group	12.1	13.2	11.9	14.3	14.1	12.7	11.9	13.7
Treatment Group	15.2	17.1	18.3	17.6	18.8	16.8	17.3	17.5

6. A restaurant wants to find out about the satisfaction of its customers. The manager asks each customer to voluntarily fill out a quick survey at the end of his or her meal. What type of sample is described?

   Ⓐ stratified sample

   Ⓑ systematic sample

   Ⓒ self-selected sample

   Ⓓ cluster sample

7. Select all the situations where the numerical value is a statistic.

   Ⓐ The average wait time of all the rides at an amusement park is 45 minutes.

   Ⓑ A survey found that the median salary of 260 web developers is about $75,580.

   Ⓒ A survey of all the teachers at a school found that the mean planning time is 54 minutes per day.

   Ⓓ A survey of 2400 adults in the United States found that 81% use the Internet daily.

Chapter 9

Test Prep (continued)

8. Select all the functions that have the same asymptotes as $f(x) = \dfrac{2}{x + 3} - 4$.

Ⓐ $g(x) = \dfrac{12}{3 + x} - 4$

Ⓑ $k(x) = \dfrac{1}{x - 3} - 4$

Ⓒ $m(x) = \dfrac{9}{x + 4} - 3$

Ⓓ $n(x) = \dfrac{-6}{x + 3} - 4$

Ⓔ $p(x) = \dfrac{5}{2x + 6} - 4$

9. You use technology to simulate rolling a six-sided die 20 times. The results are shown in the bar graph. What proportion of the 20 rolls resulted in an even number?

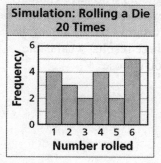

Ⓐ 60%

Ⓑ 50%

Ⓒ 55%

Ⓓ 40%

10. Which research topic is best investigated through an experiment?

Ⓐ A researcher wants to know whether liquid nitrogen fertilizer increases the growth of trees.

Ⓑ A candy company wants to know whether more teenagers or adults buy their product.

Ⓒ You want to know whether apartments on a lower floor have a higher monthly rent.

Ⓓ A researcher wants to know whether taking an SAT prep class improves SAT scores.

11. The area of the triangle is 66 square units. What is the value of x?

Ⓐ $x = -8 + \sqrt{130}$

Ⓑ $x = 6$

Ⓒ $x = 116$ and $x = 132$

Ⓓ $x = 6$ and $x = -22$

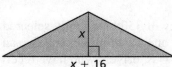

Chapter 9 **Test Prep** (continued)

12. You want to choose a cable company. Four companies service your neighborhood, offering identical packages at the same price. You survey several neighbors who have cable by asking whether they are satisfied with their cable company. The table shows the results of the survey. Based on these results, what cable company should you choose?

Company	Satisfied	Not Satisfied
1	卌							
2								
3	卌						
4	卌	||

Ⓐ Company 1

Ⓑ Company 2

Ⓒ Company 3

Ⓓ Company 4

13. A fitness tracker is $200. The value of the fitness tracker decreases by 30% each year. After how many years will the value of the fitness tracker be $68.60?

yr

14. The equation $x^3 + 8x^2 + 11x + k = 0$ has a solution of $x = -5$. What is the value of k?

$k = $

15. In a recent survey of 3500 randomly selected U.S. drivers, 62% said they had received at least one speeding ticket. Give an interval that is likely to contain the exact percent of U.S. drivers who have received at least one speeding ticket.

_____

10.1 Extra Practice

In Exercises 1 and 2, evaluate the six trigonometric functions of the angle θ.

1.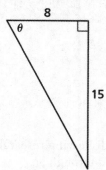

2.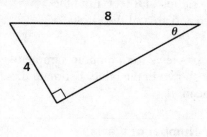

In Exercises 3 and 4, let θ be an acute angle of a right triangle. Evaluate the other five trigonometric functions of θ.

3. $\sin \theta = \dfrac{3}{19}$

4. $\tan \theta = \dfrac{3}{8}$

In Exercises 5 and 6, find the value of x for the right triangle.

5.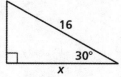

6.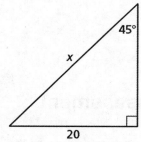

7. A parasailer is attached to a boat with a rope that is 80 feet long. The angle of elevation from the boat to the parasailer is 36°. Estimate the parasailer's height above the boat.

8. A passenger in a helicopter sees two islands directly to the left of the helicopter. What is the distance *y* between the two islands? Explain the process you used to find your answer.

Name _____ Date _____

10.1 Review & Refresh

1. A circle has a radius of 8 feet. Find the circumference and area of the circle.

2. The numbers of views for a random sample of 35 videos are shown in the table. Estimate the population mean μ.

Number of Views						
570	487	358	612	704	597	384
603	914	685	537	836	907	246
389	913	601	302	423	704	610
900	868	457	541	472	653	876
913	906	814	777	315	769	1082

In Exercises 3–6, graph the function.

3. $g(x) = \frac{1}{4}(x - 3)^3$ 4. $f(x) = -e^{x/2}$

5. $y = \sqrt{-x} + 2$ 6. $y = 3(x + 1)^2 - 2$

7. Determine whether the following research topic is best investigated through an experiment or an observational study. Then describe the design of the experiment or observational study.

   You want to know whether drinking a cup of tea before bed reduces the amount of time it takes a person to fall asleep.

8. Find the value of y for the right triangle.

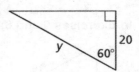

10.1 Self-Assessment

Use the scale to rate your understanding of the learning target and the success criteria.

1 I do not understand.	**2** I can do it with help.	**3** I can do it on my own.	**4** I can teach someone else.

	Rating	Date
10.1 Right Triangle Trigonometry		
Learning Target: Understand the six trigonometric functions.	1 2 3 4	
I can define the six trigonometric functions.	1 2 3 4	
I can evaluate trigonometric functions.	1 2 3 4	
I can use trigonometric functions to find side lengths of right triangles.	1 2 3 4	

10.2 Extra Practice

In Exercises 1 and 2, draw an angle in standard position having the given measure.

1. $260°$

2. $-750°$

In Exercises 3–6, convert the degree measure to radians or the radian measure to degrees.

3. $54°$

4. $-310°$

5. $\dfrac{16\pi}{15}$

6. $-\dfrac{2\pi}{5}$

7. Using radian measure, give one positive angle and one negative angle that are coterminal with the angle shown. Justify your answers.

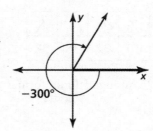

8. A dog is leashed to the corner of a house.

   a. How much running area does the dog have?

   b. You want to put fencing along the perimeter of the dog's running area. You do not put fencing along the sides of the house. How many feet of fencing do you need?

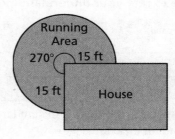

9. Consider the analog clock. Through what angle does the tip of the minute hand rotate from 8:00 A.M. to 3:00 P.M.? Give your answer in both degrees and radians.

10.2 Review & Refresh

1. Convert $220°$ to radians.

2. Evaluate the six trigonometric functions of the angle θ.

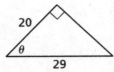

3. Complete the inequality 5 ____ $|x + 3|$ with $<$, $\le$, $>$, or $\ge$ so that $x = -10$ and $x = 2$ are both solutions of the inequality.

4. Estimate the margin of error for a survey that has a sample size of 362. Round your answer to the nearest tenth of a percent.

5. Use finite differences to determine the degree of the polynomial function that fits the data. Then use technology to find the polynomial function.

x	−2	0	2	4	6	8
f(x)	−2	2	10	22	38	58

6. Rewrite $6^2 = 36$ in logarithmic form.

7. A car dealership has 18 vehicles. The types of vehicles are shown. A vehicle is randomly selected to be featured by the dealership. What is the probability that a truck is selected?

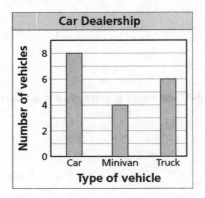

8. Write a polynomial function f of least degree that has rational coefficients, a leading coefficient of 1, and zeros of -1, 2, and $2i$.

9. Multiply $6i$ and $(5 + 2i)$. Write the answer in standard form.

10. Solve $x^{2/3} - 16 = 0$. Check your solution.

10.2 Self-Assessment

Use the scale to rate your understanding of the learning target and the success criteria.

| 1 | I do not understand. | 2 | I can do it with help. | 3 | I can do it on my own. | 4 | I can teach someone else. |

	Rating	Date
10.2 Angles and Radian Measure		
Learning Target: Draw angles in standard position and understand radian measure.	1 2 3 4	
I can draw angles in standard position.	1 2 3 4	
I can explain the meaning of radian measure.	1 2 3 4	
I can convert between degrees and radians.	1 2 3 4	
I can use radian measure to find arc lengths and the area of a sector.	1 2 3 4	

Name_____ Date_____

10.3 Extra Practice

In Exercises 1 and 2, evaluate the six trigonometric functions of θ.

1.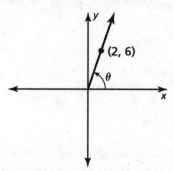

2.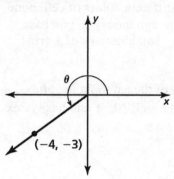

In Exercises 3 and 4, use the unit circle to evaluate the six trigonometric functions of θ.

3. $\theta = -90°$

4. $\theta = 4\pi$

In Exercises 5 and 6, sketch the angle. Then find its reference angle.

5. $-310°$

6. $\dfrac{27\pi}{10}$

In Exercises 7 and 8, evaluate the function without using technology.

7. $\tan\dfrac{4\pi}{3}$

8. $\csc 150°$

9. The horizontal distance d (in feet) traveled by a projectile launched at an angle θ and with an initial speed v (in feet per second) is given by $d = \dfrac{v^2}{32}\sin 2\theta$.

   Estimate the horizontal distance traveled by a soccer ball that is kicked at an angle of $60°$ with an initial speed of 80 feet per second.

10. An isosceles triangle has side lengths (in inches) of 7, 7, and d. The triangle has an obtuse interior angle of 115 degrees. Find d.

Name _____ Date _____

1. A store offers 12 different colors of cellphone grips. You have enough money to purchase 3 grips. How many combinations of 3 grips are possible?

2. Write an equation of the parabola in vertex form that passes through $(0, 5)$ and has vertex $(-4, -7)$.

3. Find the value of x for the right triangle.

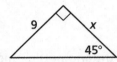

4. Sketch $-150°$. Then find its reference angle.

5. Let $f(x) = \sqrt{2x + 7}$ and $g(x) = -x^2 + 1$. Find $f(g(2))$.

6. Write an equation of the parabola.

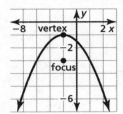

7. Using radian measure, give one positive angle and one negative angle that are coterminal with the angle shown. Justify your answers.

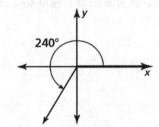

8. Find $(3x^2 - 29x + 40) \div (x - 8)$.

9. Find $\dfrac{5x}{3x - 6} - \dfrac{2x + 6}{3x - 6}$.

Use the scale to rate your understanding of the learning target and the success criteria.

| 1 | I do not understand. | 2 | I can do it with help. | 3 | I can do it on my own. | 4 | I can teach someone else. |

	Rating	Date
10.3 Trigonometric Functions of Any Angle		
Learning Target: Evaluate trigonometric functions of any angle.	1 2 3 4	
I can evaluate trigonometric functions given a point on an angle.	1 2 3 4	
I can evaluate trigonometric functions using the unit circle.	1 2 3 4	
I can find and use reference angles to evaluate trigonometric functions.	1 2 3 4	
I can solve real-life problems involving projectiles.	1 2 3 4	

Name_____ Date_____

In Exercises 1–4, identify the amplitude and period of the function. Then graph the function and describe the graph of g as a transformation of the graph of its parent function.

1. $g(x) = \sin 2x$

2. $g(x) = \frac{1}{3}\cos 2x$

3. $g(x) = 4\sin 2\pi x$

4. $g(x) = \frac{1}{2}\cos 3\pi x$

In Exercises 5–8, graph the function.

5. $g(x) = \sin \frac{1}{2}(x - \pi) + 1$

6. $g(x) = \cos\left(x + \frac{\pi}{2}\right) - 3$

7. $g(x) = -3\sin x - 2$

8. $g(x) = -\cos\left(x - \frac{\pi}{4}\right) + 2$

9. Describe a transformation of the graph of $f(x) = \cos x$ that results in the graph of $g(x) = -5\sin x$.

10.4 Review & Refresh

1. Simplify $\dfrac{x^4 - 6x^3 - 16x^2}{x^2 - 6x - 16}$.

In Exercises 2 and 3, perform the operation.

2. $(2x + 1)(x - 5)(x + 2)$

3. $(2x^4 - 3x^2 + 5x + 1) - (5x^4 + 4x^2 - 6)$

4. The table shows the numbers y (in hundreds) of subscribers to a blog after x months. Write a function that models the data. Then use your model to predict the number of subscribers after 1 year.

x	1	2	3	4	5	6	7
y	4	6	8	12	16	23	32

In Exercises 5 and 6, graph the function.

5. $g(x) = -\sin x + 1$ 6. $g(x) = 3\cos 2x$

In Exercises 7 and 8, convert the degree measure to radians or the radian measure to degrees.

7. $-25°$

8. $\dfrac{4\pi}{9}$

9. Events A and B are independent. Let $P(A \text{ and } B) = 0.54$ and $P(A) = 0.9$. Find $P(B)$.

10. Solve $8x^2 - 2x - 15 = 0$.

11. Graph the system of quadratic inequalities.

$$y > -x^2 + 1$$
$$y \le x^2 + 3x - 1$$

12. Evaluate the six trigonometric functions of θ.

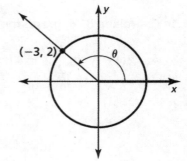

10.4 Self-Assessment

Use the scale to rate your understanding of the learning target and the success criteria.

| 1 | I do not understand. | 2 | I can do it with help. | 3 | I can do it on my own. | 4 | I can teach someone else. |

	Rating	Date
10.4 Graphing Sine and Cosine Functions		
Learning Target: Describe and graph sine and cosine functions.	1 2 3 4	
I can identify characteristics of sine and cosine functions.	1 2 3 4	
I can graph transformations of sine and cosine functions.	1 2 3 4	

Name_____ Date_____

10.5 Extra Practice

In Exercises 1–8, graph one period of the function. Describe the graph of *g* as a transformation of the graph of its parent function.

1. $g(x) = \tan 2x$

2. $g(x) = 2 \cot \dfrac{1}{2}x$

3. $g(x) = \dfrac{1}{4} \tan \dfrac{\pi}{4}x$

4. $g(x) = \dfrac{1}{2} \cot 3x$

5. $g(x) = 4 \csc x$

6. $g(x) = 2 \sec 2x$

7. $g(x) = \csc 2\pi x$

8. $g(x) = 6 \sec \dfrac{1}{4}x$

9. Let $f(x) = 9 \cot x$. The graph of *g* is a vertical shrink by a factor of $\dfrac{1}{3}$ and a reflection in the *x*-axis of the graph of *f*. Write a rule for *g*.

Name _____ Date _____

1. Find one positive angle and one negative angle that are coterminal with 48°.

2. Find the amplitude and period of the graph of the function.

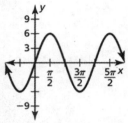

3. A wire rope can safely support a weight W (in tons) provided $W \leq 8d^2$, where d is the diameter (in inches) of the rope. Graph the inequality and interpret the solution.

4. Simplify $e^{-6} \cdot e^{18}$.

5. Graph one period of the function $g(x) = \frac{1}{2}\csc x$. Describe the graph of g as a transformation of the graph of its parent function.

6. Solve $\dfrac{3}{2x - 1} = \dfrac{6}{3 - x}$.

7. Graph the function $f(x) = \dfrac{x + 3}{x - 4}$. Find the domain and range.

8. Solve $x^2 - 7x - 30 = 0$.

10.5 **Self-Assessment**

Use the scale to rate your understanding of the learning target and the success criteria.

1 I do not understand.	2 I can do it with help.	3 I can do it on my own.	4 I can teach someone else.

	Rating	Date
10.5 Graphing Other Trigonometric Functions		
Learning Target: Describe and graph tangent, cotangent, secant, and cosecant functions.	1 2 3 4	
I can identify characteristics of tangent, cotangent, secant, and cosecant functions.	1 2 3 4	
I can graph tangent and cotangent functions.	1 2 3 4	
I can graph secant and cosecant functions.	1 2 3 4	

Name_____ Date _____

Extra Practice

1. An alternating current generator (AC generator) converts motion to electricity by generating sinusoidal voltage. Assuming that there is no vertical offset and phase shift, the voltage oscillates between −170 volts and +170 volts with a frequency of 60 hertz (cycles per second). Write and graph a sine model that gives the voltage V as a function of the time t (in seconds).

In Exercises 2–5, write a function for the sinusoid.

2.

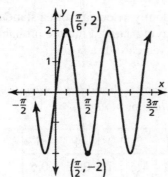

3.

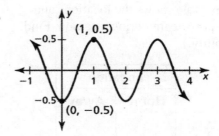

4.

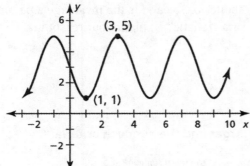

5.

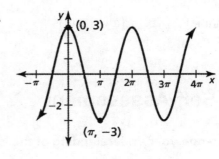

6. The table shows the average high temperature T (in degrees Fahrenheit) in Des Moines, Iowa each month, where $m = 1$ represents January. Write a model that gives T as a function of m and interpret the period of its graph.

m	1	2	3	4	5	6	7	8	9	10	11	12
T	31	36	49	62	72	82	86	84	76	63	48	34

10.6 Review & Refresh

In Exercises 1 and 2, expand the logarithmic expression.

1. $\ln xyz$

2. $\log_3 \dfrac{6}{x^3}$

3. Use the unit circle to evaluate the six trigonometric functions of $\theta = -\dfrac{\pi}{3}$.

4. The two-way table shows the locations and scores of a sports team during a season. Find each probability.

		Location	
		Home	**Away**
Score	**Win**	5	3
	Lose	2	3
	Tie	0	1

   a. $P(\text{lose}|\text{home})$ **b.** $P(\text{away}|\text{win})$

5. Write a function for the sinusoid.

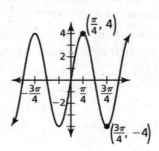

6. Simplify $\dfrac{2}{\sqrt{5}+3}$.

7. A card is randomly selected from a standard deck of 52 playing cards. Find the probability of selecting a red card *or* a spade.

8. Tell whether x and y show *direct variation*, *inverse variation*, or *neither*.

x	1	2	3	4	5
y	3	1.5	1	0.75	0.6

9. The mean age of all the dogs in an animal shelter is 3 years. Is the mean age a parameter or a statistic? Explain your reasoning.

10.6 Self-Assessment

Use the scale to rate your understanding of the learning target and the success criteria.

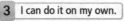

1 I do not understand.	**2** I can do it with help.	**3** I can do it on my own.	**4** I can teach someone else.

	Rating	Date
10.6 Modeling with Trigonometric Functions		
Learning Target: Write trigonometric functions.	1 2 3 4	
I can write and graph trigonometric functions using frequency.	1 2 3 4	
I can write trigonometric functions for a given graph.	1 2 3 4	
I can find a trigonometric model for a set of data using technology.	1 2 3 4	

Name_____ Date _____

In Exercises 1–4, find the values of the other five trigonometric functions of θ.

1. $\sin \theta = \dfrac{1}{5}, \; \dfrac{\pi}{2} < \theta < \pi$

2. $\cos \theta = -\dfrac{4}{5}, \; \pi < \theta < \dfrac{3\pi}{2}$

3. $\cot \theta = \dfrac{4}{7}, \; 0 < \theta < \dfrac{\pi}{2}$

4. $\sec \theta = \dfrac{\sqrt{13}}{3}, \; \dfrac{3\pi}{2} < \theta < 2\pi$

In Exercises 5–8, simplify the expression.

5. $-\dfrac{\tan \theta}{\sec \theta}$

6. $\cos\left(\dfrac{\pi}{2} - \theta\right)\left(1 - \cos^2 \theta\right)$

7. $\dfrac{2 \sec^2 x - 2 \tan^2 x}{\tan(-x)\cos(-x)}$

8. $\dfrac{-\sin\left(\dfrac{\pi}{2} - \theta\right)}{\sec(-\theta)} - \sin^2 \theta$

In Exercises 9–11, verify the identity.

9. $\dfrac{1 - \cos^2 \theta}{\sec^2 \theta} - \sin^2 \theta = -\sin^4 \theta$

10. $\csc x + \cot x = \dfrac{\sin x}{1 - \cos x}$

11. $\ln\left|\csc \theta\right| + \ln\left|\tan \theta\right| = -\ln\left|\cos \theta\right|$

10.7 Review & Refresh

1. The motion of a pendulum can be modeled by the function $d = 3 \cos 6\pi t$, where d is the horizontal displacement (in inches) of the pendulum relative to its position at rest and t is the time (in seconds). Find and interpret the period and amplitude. Then graph the function.

3. Write a function for the sinusoid.

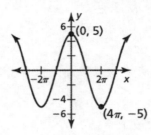

4. A normal distribution has a mean of 15 and a standard deviation of 2. Find the probability that a randomly selected x-value from the distribution is between 11 and 17.

5. Verify the identity
$$\sin^2 x + \sin^2 x \cot^2 x = 1.$$

2. You throw a dart at the board shown. Your dart is equally likely to hit any point inside the square board. Find the probability that your dart lands in the black region.

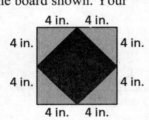

6. Evaluate $8^{4/3}$ without using technology.

10.7 Self-Assessment

Use the scale to rate your understanding of the learning target and the success criteria.

| 1 | I do not understand. | 2 | I can do it with help. | 3 | I can do it on my own. | 4 | I can teach someone else. |

	Rating	Date
10.7 Using Trigonometric Identities		
Learning Target: Use trigonometric identities to evaluate trigonometric functions and simplify trigonometric expressions.	1 2 3 4	
I can evaluate trigonometric functions using trigonometric identities.	1 2 3 4	
I can simplify trigonometric expressions using trigonometric identities.	1 2 3 4	
I can verify trigonometric identities.	1 2 3 4	

Name_____ Date_____

10.8 Extra Practice

In Exercises 1–4, find the exact value of the expression.

1. $\sin(-75°)$

2. $\tan 120°$

3. $\cos\left(-\dfrac{7\pi}{12}\right)$

4. $\cos\dfrac{35\pi}{12}$

In Exercises 5–8, evaluate the expression given that $\sin a = -\dfrac{4}{5}$ with $\pi < a < \dfrac{3\pi}{2}$ and $\cos b = \dfrac{5}{13}$ with $0 < b < \dfrac{\pi}{2}$.

5. $\cos(a - b)$

6. $\sin(a + b)$

7. $\tan(a + b)$

8. $\tan(a - b)$

In Exercises 9–12, simplify the expression.

9. $\sin\left(x + \dfrac{\pi}{2}\right)$

10. $\tan(x - 2\pi)$

11. $\cos(x - 2\pi)$

12. $\cos\left(x + \dfrac{5\pi}{2}\right)$

In Exercises 13–16, solve the equation for $0 \le x < 2\pi$.

13. $5\tan x + 5 = 0$

14. $\sin\left(x + \dfrac{3\pi}{2}\right) = 1$

15. $\cos\left(x + \dfrac{\pi}{2}\right) - \cos\left(x - \dfrac{\pi}{2}\right) = -2$

16. $\sin\left(x - \dfrac{\pi}{2}\right) + \cos\left(x - \dfrac{\pi}{2}\right) = 0$

Name _____   Date _____

In Exercises 1 and 2, solve the equation.

1. $3 - \dfrac{5}{x + 4} = \dfrac{7}{2}$

2. $\dfrac{x - 1}{x + 2} = \dfrac{7}{x^2 - 4} + 1$

In Exercises 3 and 4, find the exact value of the expression.

3. $\cos 75°$ **4.** $\tan\left(-\dfrac{7\pi}{12}\right)$

5. Find the value of x for the right triangle.

6. Simplify $\dfrac{\cos(-\theta)\,\tan\theta}{\csc\theta}$.

7. A researcher uses technology to estimate the damage that will be done if the sea level keeps rising. Identify the method of data collection.

8. Graph one period of $g(x) = \dfrac{1}{2}\tan 3x$.

Describe the graph of g as a transformation of the graph of $f(x) = \tan x$.

9. The crank arm and pedal of a bicycle are shown. The lowest point of the pedal is 4 inches above the ground. A cyclist pedals 3 revolutions per second. Write a model for the height h (in inches) of the pedal as a function of the time t (in seconds) given that the pedal is at its lowest point when $t = 0$.

7 in.

Use the scale to rate your understanding of the learning target and the success criteria.

| 1 | I do not understand. | 2 | I can do it with help. | 3 | I can do it on my own. | 4 | I can teach someone else. |

	Rating	Date
10.8 Using Sum and Difference Formulas		
Learning Target: Use sum and difference formulas to evaluate and simplify trigonometric expressions.	1 2 3 4	
I can evaluate trigonometric expressions using sum and difference formulas.	1 2 3 4	
I can simplify trigonometric expressions using sum and difference formulas.	1 2 3 4	
I can solve trigonometric equations using sum and difference formulas.	1 2 3 4	

Name_____ Date _____

Chapter 10 Chapter Self-Assessment

Use the scale to rate your understanding of the learning target and the success criteria.

1 I do not understand.　**2** I can do it with help.　**3** I can do it on my own.　**4** I can teach someone else.

	Rating	Date
Chapter 10 Trigonometric Ratios and Functions		
Learning Target: Understand trigonometric ratios and functions.	1　2　3　4	
I can define right triangle trigonometric functions.	1　2　3　4	
I can evaluate trigonometric functions of any angle.	1　2　3　4	
I can graph trigonometric functions.	1　2　3　4	
I can model using trigonometric functions.	1　2　3　4	
10.1 Right Triangle Trigonometry		
Learning Target: Understand the six trigonometric functions.	1　2　3　4	
I can define the six trigonometric functions.	1　2　3　4	
I can evaluate trigonometric functions.	1　2　3　4	
I can use trigonometric functions to find side lengths of right triangles.	1　2　3　4	
10.2 Angles and Radian Measure		
Learning Target: Draw angles in standard position and understand radian measure.	1　2　3　4	
I can draw angles in standard position.	1　2　3　4	
I can explain the meaning of radian measure.	1　2　3　4	
I can convert between degrees and radians.	1　2　3　4	
I can use radian measure to find arc lengths and the area of a sector.	1　2　3　4	
10.3 Trigonometric Functions of Any Angle		
Learning Target: Evaluate trigonometric functions of any angle.	1　2　3　4	
I can evaluate trigonometric functions given a point on an angle.	1　2　3　4	
I can evaluate trigonometric functions using the unit circle.	1　2　3　4	
I can find and use reference angles to evaluate trigonometric functions.	1　2　3　4	
I can solve real-life problems involving projectiles.	1　2　3　4	

Chapter 10

Chapter Self-Assessment (continued)

	Rating	Date
10.4 Graphing Sine and Cosine Functions		
Learning Target: Describe and graph sine and cosine functions.	1 2 3 4	
I can identify characteristics of sine and cosine functions.	1 2 3 4	
I can graph transformations of sine and cosine functions.	1 2 3 4	
10.5 Graphing Other Trigonometric Functions		
Learning Target: Describe and graph tangent, cotangent, secant, and cosecant functions.	1 2 3 4	
I can identify characteristics of tangent, cotangent, secant, and cosecant functions.	1 2 3 4	
I can graph tangent and cotangent functions.	1 2 3 4	
I can graph secant and cosecant functions.	1 2 3 4	
10.6 Modeling with Trigonometric Functions		
Learning Target: Write trigonometric functions.	1 2 3 4	
I can write and graph trigonometric functions using frequency.	1 2 3 4	
I can write trigonometric functions for a given graph.	1 2 3 4	
I can find a trigonometric model for a set of data using technology.	1 2 3 4	
10.7 Using Trigonometric Identities		
Learning Target: Use trigonometric identities to evaluate trigonometric functions and simplify trigonometric expressions.	1 2 3 4	
I can evaluate trigonometric functions using trigonometric identities.	1 2 3 4	
I can simplify trigonometric expressions using trigonometric identities.	1 2 3 4	
I can verify trigonometric identities.	1 2 3 4	
10.8 Using Sum and Difference Formulas		
Learning Target: Use sum and difference formulas to evaluate and simplify trigonometric expressions.	1 2 3 4	
I can evaluate trigonometric expressions using sum and difference formulas.	1 2 3 4	
I can simplify trigonometric expressions using sum and difference formulas.	1 2 3 4	
I can solve trigonometric equations using sum and difference formulas.	1 2 3 4	

Chapter 10 Test Prep

1. Which function has a period of 8π and an amplitude of 7?

   Ⓐ $y = 7\cos 4x$

   Ⓑ $y = 7\sin(8x + 3)$

   Ⓒ $y = -7\sin\frac{1}{4}x + 1$

   Ⓓ $y = -8\pi\cos 7x$

2. You flip a coin and roll a six-sided die. What is the probability that the coin shows heads and the die shows an even number?

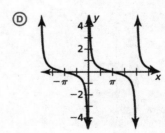

3. Which graph represents the function $g(x) = \frac{1}{3}\cot\frac{1}{2}x$?

   Ⓐ
   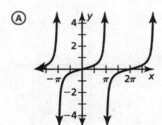

   Ⓑ

   Ⓒ
   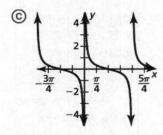

   Ⓓ

4. Write a polynomial function f of least degree that has rational coefficients, a leading coefficient of 1, and the zeros 4, $-\sqrt{5}$, and -5.

_____

Chapter 10 Test Prep (continued)

5. Write a function for the sinusoid.

_____

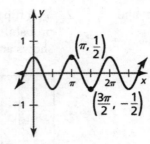

$\left(\pi, \dfrac{1}{2}\right)$

$\left(\dfrac{3\pi}{2}, -\dfrac{1}{2}\right)$

6. Which system has no solution?

Ⓐ $y = -2x^2 - 6$
$y = -(x - 3)^2 + 8$

Ⓑ $8x + y = -2x^2 - 8$
$x^2 - y - 6x = -10$

Ⓒ $y = 2x + 5$
$x^2 + y^2 = 5$

Ⓓ $y - 4x = x^2$
$-8x - 4y = 20$

7. A researcher places mold samples in two different climates. The researcher then measures the mold growth in each sample after 1 week. What method of data collection did the researcher use?

Ⓐ experiment

Ⓑ observational study

Ⓒ survey

Ⓓ simulation

8. A radio transmission tower at your local television station is 130 feet tall. How long should a guy wire be if it is attached 14 feet below the top of the tower making a 30° angle with the ground?

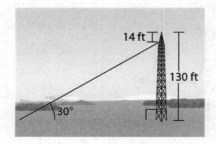

14 ft

130 ft

30°

Chapter 10 Test Prep (continued)

9. Let g be a horizontal stretch by a factor of 5, followed by a translation 6 units right of the graph of $f(x) = \sqrt{10x}$. Which of the following is a rule for g?

Ⓐ $g(x) = \sqrt{2x - 12}$

Ⓑ $g(x) = \sqrt{50x - 6}$

Ⓒ $g(x) = \sqrt{50x - 300}$

Ⓓ $g(x) = 5\sqrt{10x - 60}$

10. A professional football team leads at halftime in 40% of the games in a season. The team wins 90% of the time when leading at halftime, but only 20% of the time when not leading at halftime. What is the probability that the team wins a particular game in the season?

11. Select all the solutions of
$$\sin(x + \pi) = -\frac{1}{2} \text{ for } 0 \le x < 2\pi.$$

Ⓐ $x = \dfrac{\pi}{6}$

Ⓑ $x = \dfrac{5\pi}{6}$

Ⓒ $x = \dfrac{7\pi}{6}$

Ⓓ $x = \dfrac{11\pi}{6}$

Ⓔ $x = \dfrac{13\pi}{6}$

12. Select all the angles that are coterminal with $-130°$.

Ⓐ $1210°$

Ⓑ $590°$

Ⓒ $-850°$

Ⓓ $\dfrac{23\pi}{18}$

Ⓔ $\dfrac{5\pi}{18}$

Ⓕ $-\dfrac{49\pi}{18}$

Chapter 10 **Test Prep** (continued)

13. Given that $\sin \theta = \dfrac{3}{8}$ and $\dfrac{\pi}{2} < \theta < \pi$, which of the following is *not* a trigonometric function of θ?

Ⓐ $\cot \theta = -\dfrac{\sqrt{55}}{3}$

Ⓑ $\cos \theta = \dfrac{\sqrt{55}}{8}$

Ⓒ $\tan \theta = -\dfrac{3\sqrt{55}}{55}$

Ⓓ $\csc \theta = \dfrac{8}{3}$

14. What is the ratio of the perimeter to the area of the triangle?

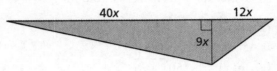

Ⓐ $\dfrac{13x}{3}$

Ⓑ $\dfrac{13}{3x}$

Ⓒ $\dfrac{13x}{6}$

Ⓓ $\dfrac{6}{13x}$

15. In what quadrant does the terminal side of θ lie when $\cot \theta > 0$ and $\cos \theta < 0$?

Ⓐ Quadrant I

Ⓑ Quadrant II

Ⓒ Quadrant III

Ⓓ Quadrant IV

16. The table shows the numbers of rabbits r in a forest t years after a forest fire. How many years will it take for the rabbit population to surpass 20,000? Round your answer to the nearest hundredth.

t	0	1	2	3	4	5
r	20	60	180	540	1620	4860

yr

Name_____ Date_____

In Exercises 1 and 2, write the first six terms of the sequence.

1. $a_n = n^3 - 1$

2. $f(n) = (-2)^{n-1}$

In Exercises 3–6, describe the pattern, write the next term, and write a rule for the nth term of the sequence.

3. $-3, -1, 1, 3, \ldots$

4. $-3.2, -2.6, -2, -1.4, \ldots$

5. $\dfrac{2}{5}, \dfrac{4}{5}, \dfrac{6}{5}, \dfrac{8}{5}, \ldots$

6. $\dfrac{11}{6}, \dfrac{11}{7}, \dfrac{11}{8}, \dfrac{11}{9}, \ldots$

7. For an exercise program, you do 20 jumping jacks the first week. Each week, you do 5 more jumping jacks than the previous week. Write a rule for the number of jumping jacks you do each week. Then graph the sequence.

In Exercises 8 and 9, write the series using summation notation.

8. $-1 + 4 - 9 + 16 - 25 + \cdots$

9. $\dfrac{5}{7} + \dfrac{4}{7} + \dfrac{3}{7} + \dfrac{2}{7} + \cdots$

In Exercises 10–13, find the sum.

10. $\displaystyle\sum_{i=1}^{4} (4i - 3)$

11. $\displaystyle\sum_{n=2}^{5} \dfrac{n}{n-1}$

12. $\displaystyle\sum_{k=5}^{16} 1$

13. $\displaystyle\sum_{i=1}^{20} i^2$

14. You want to save $300 for a new game system. You begin by saving a dime on the first day. You save an additional dime each day after that.

    a. How much money will you have saved after 50 days?

    b. Use a series to determine how many days it takes you to save $300.

11.1 Review & Refresh

1. Solve the system.

$x + y + 2z = -3$

$3x + 2y - z = 2$

$-x - 4z = 1$

In Exercises 2 and 3, write the series using summation notation. Then find the sum of the series.

2. $\frac{4}{5} + 1 + \frac{6}{5} + \frac{7}{5} + \cdots + 2$

3. $15 + 24 + 35 + 48 + \cdots + 143$

4. The numbers of photographs stored on the cell phones of a random sample of 30 cell phone users are shown in the table. Estimate the population mean μ.

Number of Photographs					
372	782	841	1243	926	1011
918	912	812	716	821	900
1083	814	943	1356	648	1234
599	987	927	984	973	874
602	751	837	963	918	852

5. A florist has 20 different types of flowers. How many combinations of 4 flowers are possible?

In Exercises 6 and 7, find the sum or difference.

6. $\frac{6}{5x} + \frac{2}{5x}$

7. $\frac{4}{x-1} - \frac{9}{x+1}$

8. Complete the square for $x^2 - 10x$. Then factor the trinomial.

9. Evaluate the six trigonometric functions of θ.

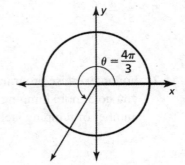

10. Write a function for the sinusoid.

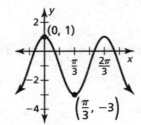

11.1 Self-Assessment

Use the scale to rate your understanding of the learning target and the success criteria.

| 1 | I do not understand. | 2 | I can do it with help. | 3 | I can do it on my own. | 4 | I can teach someone else. |

	Rating	Date
11.1 Defining and Using Sequences and Series		
Learning Target: Understand sequences and series.	1 2 3 4	
I can use rules to write terms of sequences.	1 2 3 4	
I can write rules for sequences.	1 2 3 4	
I can write and find sums of series.	1 2 3 4	

Name_____ Date _____

11.2 Extra Practice

In Exercises 1–4, determine whether the sequence is arithmetic. Explain your reasoning.

1. 1, 4, 7, 12, 17, …

2. 26, 23, 20, 17, 14, …

3. 0.3, 0.5, 0.7, 0.9, 1,1, …

4. $\dfrac{1}{2}, \dfrac{1}{4}, \dfrac{1}{6}, \dfrac{1}{8}, \dfrac{1}{10}, \cdots$

In Exercises 5–8, write a rule for the *n*th term of the sequence. Then find a_{20}.

5. 3, 9, 15, 21, …

6. 8, 3, −2, −7, …

7. $-1, -\dfrac{1}{2}, 0, \dfrac{1}{2}, \cdots$

8. 0.7, 0.2, −0.3, −0.8, …

9. Write a rule for the *n*th term of the sequence with $a_{12} = -13$ and $d = -2$. Then graph the first six terms of the sequence.

In Exercises 10 and 11, write a rule for the *n*th term of the arithmetic sequence.

10. $a_8 = 59, a_{13} = 99$

11. $a_{18} = -5, a_{27} = -8$

In Exercises 12–14, find the sum.

12. $\displaystyle\sum_{i=1}^{47} (4i + 7)$

13. $\displaystyle\sum_{i=1}^{22} (5 - 2i)$

14. $\displaystyle\sum_{i=1}^{38} (0.8i + 4.6)$

15. The expressions $2x - 2$, x, $2x + 1$ are the first three terms of an arithmetic sequence. Find the value of x and the next term of the sequence.

Name _____ Date _____

In Exercises 1 and 2, simplify the expression.

1. $\dfrac{5^{1/4}}{5}$

2. $10^{1/3} \cdot 10^{1/2}$

3. The graph of a polynomial function is shown. Is the degree of the function *odd* or *even*? Is the leading coefficient of the function *positive* or *negative*?

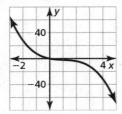

4. One term of an arithmetic sequence is $a_8 = 22$. The common difference is $d = 4$.

   a. Write a rule for the nth term. Then graph the first six terms of the sequence.

   b. Find the sum of the first 8 terms.

5. You and your friend enter a drawing to win a gift card. From 45 entries, 2 winners are randomly selected. What is the probability that you and your friend win?

6. Determine whether the functions f and g are inverses. Explain your reasoning.

x	-10	-5	0	5	10
$f(x)$	15	9	3	-3	-9

x	15	9	3	-3	-9
$g(x)$	-10	-5	0	5	10

7. Given that $\sin\theta = -\dfrac{5}{13}$ and $\pi < \theta < \dfrac{3\pi}{2}$, find the values of the other five trigonometric functions of θ.

8. Find the sum $\displaystyle\sum_{k=1}^{5}\left(18 - k^3\right)$.

Use the scale to rate your understanding of the learning target and the success criteria.

| 1 | I do not understand. | 2 | I can do it with help. | 3 | I can do it on my own. | 4 | I can teach someone else. |

	Rating	Date
11.2 Analyzing Arithmetic Sequences and Series		
Learning Target: Analyze arithmetic sequences and series.	1 2 3 4	
I can identify arithmetic sequences.	1 2 3 4	
I can write rules for arithmetic sequences.	1 2 3 4	
I can find sums of finite arithmetic series.	1 2 3 4	

Name_____ Date_____

11.3 Extra Practice

In Exercises 1–4, determine whether the sequence is geometric. Explain your reasoning.

1. 4, 12, 36, 108, 324, …

2. 45, 40, 35, 30, 25, …

3. 1.3, 7.8, 46.8, 280.8, 1684.8, …

4. $\dfrac{3}{2}, -\dfrac{3}{4}, \dfrac{3}{8}, -\dfrac{3}{16}, \dfrac{3}{32}, \dots$

In Exercises 5–8, write a rule for the nth term of the sequence. Then find a_6.

5. 6, 18, 54, 162, …

6. 3, −6, 12, −24, …

7. $1, \dfrac{5}{2}, \dfrac{25}{4}, \dfrac{125}{8}, \dots$

8. −2.4, −16.8, −117.6, −823.2, …

9. Write a rule for the nth term of the sequence with $a_8 = 384$ and $r = 2$. Then graph the first six terms of the sequence.

In Exercises 10 and 11, write a rule for the nth term of the geometric sequence.

10. $a_3 = 54$, $a_6 = 1458$

11. $a_2 = -2$, $a_5 = \dfrac{2}{125}$

In Exercises 12–14, find the sum.

12. $\displaystyle\sum_{i=1}^{7} 3(-4)^{i-1}$

13. $\displaystyle\sum_{i=1}^{8} 5\left(\dfrac{2}{3}\right)^{i-1}$

14. $\displaystyle\sum_{i=0}^{10} 3\left(\dfrac{3}{2}\right)^{i-1}$

15. Use the rule for the sum of a finite geometric series to write
$5x^2 + 20x^4 + 80x^6 + 320x^8 + 1280x^{10}$ as a rational expression.

11.3 Review & Refresh

1. Find the discriminant of $3x^2 + 8x - 1 = 0$, and describe the number and type of solutions of the equation.

2. Determine whether the study is a randomized comparative experiment. If it is, describe the treatment, the treatment group, and the control group. If it is not, explain why not and discuss whether the conclusions drawn from the study are valid.

Online Ordering
Order Faster on New Website
To test its new website, a company randomly selected and divided 218 individuals into two groups. One group used the new website and the other group used the old website. Users of the new website completed their orders 15% faster.

3. Describe the transformation of $f(x) = 6^x$ represented by $g(x) = 6^{x+4}$.

4. Simplify the expression $\cos\left(x - \dfrac{5\pi}{2}\right)$.

5. Find the sum $\displaystyle\sum_{k=3}^{7} (17 - 4k)$.

6. Write a rule for the sequence with the given terms.

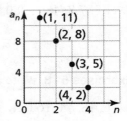

7. Write a rule for the nth term of the sequence with $a_4 = 250$ and $r = 5$. Then graph the first six terms of the sequence.

8. Each section of the spinner has the same area. What is the probability of spinning an even number *or* a factor of 5?

11.3 Self-Assessment

Use the scale to rate your understanding of the learning target and the success criteria.

1	I do not understand.	2	I can do it with help.	3	I can do it on my own.	4	I can teach someone else.

	Rating	Date
11.3 Analyzing Geometric Sequences and Series		
Learning Target: Analyze geometric sequences and series.	1 2 3 4	
I can identify geometric sequences.	1 2 3 4	
I can write rules for geometric sequences.	1 2 3 4	
I can find sums of finite geometric series.	1 2 3 4	

Name_____ Date _____

11.4 Extra Practice

In Exercises 1 and 2, consider the infinite geometric series. Find and graph the partial sums S_n for $n = 1, 2, 3, 4,$ and 5. Then describe what happens to S_n as n increases.

1. $1 + \dfrac{3}{8} + \dfrac{9}{64} + \dfrac{27}{512} + \dfrac{81}{4096} + \cdots$

2. $3 + \dfrac{3}{5} + \dfrac{3}{25} + \dfrac{3}{125} + \dfrac{3}{625} + \cdots$

In Exercises 3–6, find the sum of the infinite geometric series, if it exists.

3. $\displaystyle\sum_{n=1}^{\infty} 6\left(\dfrac{3}{5}\right)^{n-1}$

4. $\displaystyle\sum_{i=1}^{\infty} \dfrac{10}{3}\left(\dfrac{5}{2}\right)^{i-1}$

5. $5 + \dfrac{5}{3} + \dfrac{5}{9} + \dfrac{5}{27} + \cdots$

6. $\dfrac{1}{2} - \dfrac{1}{4} + \dfrac{1}{8} - \dfrac{1}{16} + \cdots$

7. You push a saucer swing one time and then allow it to swing freely. On the first swing, the saucer travels a distance of 12 feet. On each successive swing, the saucer travels 70% of the distance of the previous swing. What is the total distance the saucer travels?

8. You bounce a ball and then allow it to bounce freely. On the first bounce, the ball reaches a height of 28 inches. On each successive bounce, the ball bounces to 80% of its previous height. Starting with the first bounce, what is the total vertical distance the ball travels? (*Hint*: Be sure to consider the distance the ball travels up *and* down on each bounce.)

9. Write 0.121212… as a fraction in simplest form.

10. Write two infinite geometric series that each have a sum of 8. Justify your answers.

Name _____ Date _____

11.4 Review & Refresh

In Exercises 1–3, determine whether the sequence is *arithmetic*, *geometric*, or *neither*.

1. 41, 33, 25, 17, 9, …

2. −4, −2, 2, 8, 16, …

3. 4.5, 9, 18, 36, 72, …

4. Determine the type of function represented by the table.

x	0	2	4	6	8
y	−4	0	12	32	60

5. The seats in an auditorium are arranged in rows. The first row has 10 seats, and each subsequent row has four more seats than the previous row.

    a. Write a rule for the number of seats in the nth row.

    b. There are a total of 10 rows. How many seats are in the auditorium?

In Exercises 6–9, solve the equation.

6. $\frac{1}{9}x^2 + 3 = 2$

7. $x^3 + 2x^2 = 24x$

8. $8^x = 24$

9. $\frac{4}{x + 2} + 1 = \frac{4}{x}$

In Exercises 10 and 11, find the sum.

10. $\sum\limits_{i=3}^{9} \frac{i}{i + 3}$

11. $\sum\limits_{n=1}^{\infty} 5\left(\frac{7}{8}\right)^{n-1}$

12. Divide $2x^3 - 7x^2 + 11x - 18$ by $x - 2$.

13. The graph of g is a transformation of the graph of $f(x) = 1.5^x$. Write a rule for g.

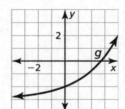

11.4 Self-Assessment

Use the scale to rate your understanding of the learning target and the success criteria.

| 1 | I do not understand. | 2 | I can do it with help. | 3 | I can do it on my own. | 4 | I can teach someone else. |

	Rating	Date
11.4 Finding Sums of Infinite Geometric Series		
Learning Target: Find partial sums and sums of infinite geometric series.	1 2 3 4	
I can find partial sums of infinite geometric series.	1 2 3 4	
I can find sums of infinite geometric series.	1 2 3 4	
I can solve real-life problems using infinite geometric series.	1 2 3 4	

11.5 Extra Practice

In Exercises 1 and 2, write the first six terms of the sequence.

1. $a_1 = 2, a_n = a_{n-1} + 5$

2. $f(0) = 1, f(n) = 2 \bullet f(n-1)$

In Exercises 3–10, write a recursive rule for the sequence.

3. $9, 12, 15, 18, 21, \ldots$

4. $50, 20, 8, \frac{16}{5}, \frac{32}{25}, \ldots$

5. $3, 4, 1, -3, -4, \ldots$

6. $3, 2, 6, 12, 72, \ldots$

7. $a_n = 5 - 3n$

8. $a_n = 10(-2)^{n-1}$

9. $a_n = -1 + 8n$

10. $a_n = -3\left(\frac{3}{4}\right)^{n-1}$

In Exercises 11–14, write an explicit rule for the sequence.

11. $a_1 = -1, a_n = a_{n-1} + 7$

12. $a_1 = 24, a_n = 0.2a_{n-1}$

13. $a_1 = 1, a_n = a_{n-1} - 0.3$

14. $a_1 = -2, a_n = -5a_{n-1}$

15. You borrow $20,000 to buy a car. The loan has a 4.8% annual interest rate that is compounded monthly for 6 years. The monthly payment is $320.25.

    a. Find the balance after the seventh payment.

    b. Find the amount of the last payment.

16. A television steaming service initially has 110,000 members. Each year, the company loses 10% of its current members and gains 8000 new members.

    a. Write a recursive rule for the number a_n of members at the start of the nth year.

    b. What happens to the number of members after an extended period of time?

Name _____ Date _____

1. Solve $\sqrt{x} - 7 = 1$.

2. Find the value of x for the right triangle.

3. The variables x and y vary inversely, and $y = \frac{1}{4}$ when $x = -24$. Write an equation that relates x and y. Then find y when $x = 3$.

4. Write a rule for the sequence with the given terms.

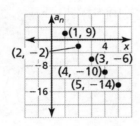

5. Find the sum $\displaystyle\sum_{i=1}^{\infty} 12(0.6)^{i-1}$.

In Exercises 6–9, graph the function.

6. $g(x) = \dfrac{2}{x}$

7. $f(x) = -\log x + 1$

8. $y = \sqrt{3x + 3} - 2$ **9.** $g(x) = -x^4 + 4$

In Exercises 10 and 11, write a recursive rule for the sequence.

10. $6, 11, 16, 21, 26, \ldots$

11. $-2, -6, -18, -54, -162, \ldots$

11.5 Self-Assessment

Use the scale to rate your understanding of the learning target and the success criteria.

| 1 | I do not understand. | 2 | I can do it with help. | 3 | I can do it on my own. | 4 | I can teach someone else. |

	Rating	Date
11.5 Using Recursive Rules with Sequences		
Learning Target: Write and use recursively defined sequences.	1 2 3 4	
I can write terms of recursively defined sequences.	1 2 3 4	
I can write recursive rules for sequences.	1 2 3 4	
I can translate between recursive rules and explicit rules.	1 2 3 4	
I can use recursive rules to solve real-life problems.	1 2 3 4	

Name_____ Date _____

Chapter Self-Assessment

Use the scale to rate your understanding of the learning target and the success criteria.

1 I do not understand.   **2** I can do it with help.   **3** I can do it on my own.   **4** I can teach someone else.

	Rating	Date
Chapter 11 Sequences and Series		
Learning Target: Understand sequences and series.	1 2 3 4	
I can define and use sequences and series.	1 2 3 4	
I can describe how to find sums of infinite geometric series.	1 2 3 4	
I can analyze arithmetic and geometric sequences and series.	1 2 3 4	
I can explain how to write recursive rules for sequences.	1 2 3 4	
11.1 Defining and Using Sequences and Series		
Learning Target: Understand sequences and series.	1 2 3 4	
I can use rules to write terms of sequences.	1 2 3 4	
I can write rules for sequences.	1 2 3 4	
I can write and find sums of series.	1 2 3 4	
11.2 Analyzing Arithmetic Sequences and Series		
Learning Target: Analyze arithmetic sequences and series.	1 2 3 4	
I can identify arithmetic sequences.	1 2 3 4	
I can write rules for arithmetic sequences.	1 2 3 4	
I can find sums of finite arithmetic series.	1 2 3 4	
11.3 Analyzing Geometric Sequences and Series		
Learning Target: Analyze geometric sequences and series.	1 2 3 4	
I can identify geometric sequences.	1 2 3 4	
I can write rules for geometric sequences.	1 2 3 4	
I can find sums of finite geometric series.	1 2 3 4	

Name _____ Date _____

Chapter Self-Assessment (continued)

	Rating	Date
11.4 Finding Sums of Infinite Geometric Series		
Learning Target: Find partial sums and sums of infinite geometric series.	1 2 3 4	
I can find partial sums of infinite geometric series.	1 2 3 4	
I can find sums of infinite geometric series.	1 2 3 4	
I can solve real-life problems using infinite geometric series.	1 2 3 4	
11.5 Using Recursive Rules with Sequences		
Learning Target: Write and use recursively defined sequences.	1 2 3 4	
I can write terms of recursively defined sequences.	1 2 3 4	
I can write recursive rules for sequences.	1 2 3 4	
I can translate between recursive rules and explicit rules.	1 2 3 4	
I can use recursive rules to solve real-life problems.	1 2 3 4	

Chapter 11 **Test Prep**

1. Write the series using summation notation.

$$\frac{1}{2} + \frac{1}{4} + \frac{1}{6} + \cdots + \frac{1}{14}$$

_____

2. Which graph has x-intercepts that are equivalent to the roots of the equation
$\left(x + \frac{1}{2}\right)^2 = \frac{9}{4}$?

Ⓐ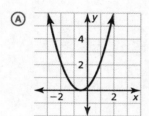

Ⓑ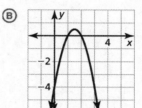

Ⓒ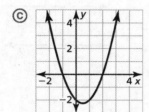

Ⓓ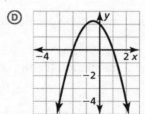

3. Evaluate $\sec\left(-\frac{\pi}{3}\right)$ without using a calculator.

$\sec\left(-\frac{\pi}{3}\right) =$

Name _____ Date _____

4. Select all the geometric sequences.

Ⓐ 2, 4, 8, 16, …

Ⓑ $\frac{2}{3}, \frac{3}{4}, \frac{4}{5}, \frac{5}{6}, \dots$

Ⓒ −20, −16, −12, −8, …

Ⓓ $\frac{1}{2}, \frac{3}{2}, \frac{9}{2}, \frac{27}{2}, \dots$

Ⓔ $\frac{15}{8}, \frac{13}{8}, \frac{11}{8}, \frac{9}{8}, \dots$

Ⓕ −1, 4, −16, 64, …

5. Select all the exponential decay functions.

Ⓐ $f(x) = (1.75)^x$

Ⓑ $g(x) = 3e^{-x}$

Ⓒ $h(x) = \left(\frac{5}{3}\right)^x$

Ⓓ $j(x) = 0.5e^x$

Ⓔ $k(x) = 4^{-x/3}$

6. Which of the following correctly describes the transformation from the graph of the parent constant function to the graph of g?

Ⓐ The graph of g is a vertical translation 5 units down of the graph of the parent function.

Ⓑ The graph of g is a vertical translation 6 units down of the graph of the parent function.

Ⓒ The graph of g is a vertical translation 7 units down of the graph of the parent function.

Ⓓ The graph of g is a vertical translation 8 units down of the graph of the parent function.

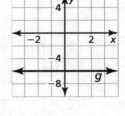

7. Simplify $\sqrt[10]{\dfrac{n^{-1}p^{22}}{n^9 p}}$.

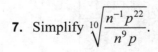

8. One term of an arithmetic sequence is $a_9 = 25$. The common difference is 4. What is another term of the sequence?

Ⓐ $a_2 = 19$

Ⓑ $a_{18} = 61$

Ⓒ $a_{20} = -19$

Ⓓ $a_{23} = -153$

Chapter 11 Test Prep (continued)

9. A greenhouse has 2000 succulents. Each year, 60% of the succulents are sold and 300 seedlings are planted. How many succulents does the greenhouse have at the start of the fourth year?

succulents

10. A company determines that the demand d for one of its products varies inversely with the price p of the product. When the price is $6.50, the demand is 910 units. When the demand is 845 units, what is the price of the product?

$

11. Which of the following series does *not* have a sum that is equal to the sum of

$$\sum_{i=1}^{4} 0.4(2)^{i-1}?$$

Ⓐ $\sum_{i=1}^{\infty} -3\left(\frac{1}{2}\right)^{i-1}$

Ⓑ $\sum_{i=1}^{\infty} 5\left(\frac{1}{6}\right)^{i-1}$

Ⓒ $\sum_{i=1}^{\infty} 2\left(\frac{2}{3}\right)^{i-1}$

Ⓓ $\sum_{i=1}^{\infty} 4\left(\frac{1}{3}\right)^{i-1}$

12. Consider the function $f(x) = x^4 - 2x^3 - 15x^2$.

For what value of k does $\dfrac{f(x)}{x - k}$ have a remainder *not* equal to 0?

Ⓐ −3

Ⓑ 0

Ⓒ 3

Ⓓ 5

Chapter 11 **Test Prep** (continued)

13. What is the 754th term of the sequence whose first term is $a_1 = 0.001$ and whose nth term is $a_n = 1.02a_{n-1}$?

Ⓐ 0

Ⓑ 768.1

Ⓒ 2991.8

Ⓓ 3051.6

14. A survey asks juniors and seniors whether they will attend a school dance. The two-way table shows the results. What is the probability that a randomly selected student from the survey is a junior who is not attending the dance?

		Attending	
		Yes	No
Class	Junior	76	35
	Senior	63	26

Ⓐ 38%

Ⓑ about 31.5%

Ⓒ 30.5%

Ⓓ 17.5%

15. You post a link to a video on your social network page. Eight of your friends repost the link, then eight of each of their friends repost the link, and so on. What is the total number of people who reposted the link after the fifth round?

_____ people

16. What is the value of n?

$$\sum_{i=1}^{n}(-3i + 8) = -203$$

$n =$

12.1 Extra Practice

In Exercises 1–4, perform the indicated operation, if possible. If not possible, explain why not.

1. $\begin{bmatrix} 2 & -1 \\ -3 & 5 \end{bmatrix} + \begin{bmatrix} 1 & -3 \\ 3 & 4 \end{bmatrix}$

2. $\begin{bmatrix} 9 & 0 \\ 1 & -5 \end{bmatrix} - \begin{bmatrix} 6 & -4 \\ 7 & -4 \end{bmatrix}$

3. $\begin{bmatrix} 4 \\ -2 \\ -2 \end{bmatrix} - \begin{bmatrix} -2 & -3 \\ 5 & 8 \end{bmatrix}$

4. $\begin{bmatrix} -3 & 12 & 4 \\ 7 & -6 & -11 \end{bmatrix} + \begin{bmatrix} 6 & -11 & 5 \\ 7 & -3 & 8 \end{bmatrix}$

In Exercises 5 and 6, perform the indicated operation.

5. $4 \begin{bmatrix} 1 & 0 \\ -5 & 6 \end{bmatrix}$

6. $\dfrac{1}{5} \begin{bmatrix} 10 & 25 \\ -5 & 50 \\ 40 & 5 \end{bmatrix}$

In Exercises 7–10, solve the matrix equation for *a*, *b*, *c*, and *d*.

7. $\begin{bmatrix} -1 & a \\ b & 2 \end{bmatrix} = \begin{bmatrix} c & 8 \\ -6 & d \end{bmatrix}$

8. $\begin{bmatrix} 2a & -9 \\ 10 & -4 \\ c-5 & 18 \end{bmatrix} = \begin{bmatrix} -8 & -9 \\ 10 & 5b \\ -2 & d \end{bmatrix}$

9. $2\left(\begin{bmatrix} -7 & a \\ 3 & 2 \end{bmatrix} + \begin{bmatrix} 1 & 3 \\ 1 & d \end{bmatrix} \right) = \begin{bmatrix} c & 12 \\ b & -10 \end{bmatrix}$

10. $\begin{bmatrix} -2 & 4a & -6 \\ 8 & 7 & 1 \end{bmatrix} - 3\begin{bmatrix} 4 & 1 & c \\ 4 & 2 & b \end{bmatrix} = \begin{bmatrix} -14 & 5 & -6 \\ -4 & d & 10 \end{bmatrix}$

11. The table shows audition results of brass and woodwind players from your school during two consecutive years. Organize the data using two matrices, one for each year. Then find and interpret a matrix that gives the change in results from 2018 to 2019 for each instrument type.

Audition Results

Result	Brass 2018	Brass 2019	Woodwind 2018	Woodwind 2019
Accepted	4	5	2	3
Rejected	6	4	2	1
Standby	0	1	1	1

Name _____   Date _____

12.1 Review & Refresh

1. Write the first six terms of the sequence.

$$a_1 = 17, a_n = a_{n-1} - 2$$

2. Find the product of $(x + 1)$ and $(x^2 - x + 2)$.

3. Let $P(A) = 0.25$, $P(B) = 0.3$, and $P(A \text{ and } B) = 0.15$. Find $P(A \text{ or } B)$.

4. Write a rule for the sequence with the given terms.

n	1	2	3	4	5
a_n	3	–6	12	–24	48

5. A park ranger records whether guests to a park visit an information booth. Identify the method of data collection.

6. A lawn sprinkler rotates 135°, as shown. Find the area watered by the sprinkler.

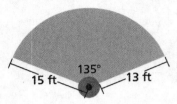

7. Find the sum of the infinite geometric series.

$$64 + 16 + 4 + \frac{1}{4} + \cdots$$

In Exercises 8 and 9, perform the indicated operation.

8. $\begin{bmatrix} 3 & 8 & -6 \end{bmatrix} + \begin{bmatrix} -1 & 6 & 2 \end{bmatrix}$

9. $-\dfrac{1}{4}\begin{bmatrix} 16 & -4 \\ 0 & 1 \end{bmatrix}$

12.1 Self-Assessment

Use the scale to rate your understanding of the learning target and the success criteria.

| 1 | I do not understand. | 2 | I can do it with help. | 3 | I can do it on my own. | 4 | I can teach someone else. |

	Rating	Date
12.1 Basic Matrix Operations		
Learning Target: Perform basic operations involving matrices.	1 2 3 4	
I can add and subtract matrices.	1 2 3 4	
I can multiply matrices by scalars.	1 2 3 4	
I can solve matrix equations.	1 2 3 4	
I can represent data in a matrix to solve real-life problems.	1 2 3 4	

Name_____ Date_____

In Exercises 1–4, determine whether the product AB is defined. If so, state the dimensions of AB.

1. $A: 3 \times 2, B: 2 \times 3$

2. $A: 1 \times 2, B: 1 \times 3$

3. $A = \begin{bmatrix} 4 \\ 0 \\ 2 \end{bmatrix}, B = \begin{bmatrix} 1 & 7 & 3 & 4 \end{bmatrix}$

4. $A = \begin{bmatrix} 2 & 4 \\ -1 & -3 \end{bmatrix}, B = \begin{bmatrix} 1 & 0 \\ 0 & 1 \end{bmatrix}$

In Exercises 5–8, find the product, if possible. If not possible, explain why not.

5. $\begin{bmatrix} 2 & -3 \end{bmatrix}\begin{bmatrix} 7 \\ 1 \end{bmatrix}$

6. $\begin{bmatrix} 1 & 5 \\ 6 & 2 \end{bmatrix}\begin{bmatrix} -1 & -4 \end{bmatrix}$

7. $\begin{bmatrix} 0 & -8 \\ -1 & -2 \end{bmatrix}\begin{bmatrix} -3 & 1 \\ 2 & 4 \end{bmatrix}$

8. $\begin{bmatrix} 4 & 0 & 1 \\ 1 & -6 & 0 \end{bmatrix}\begin{bmatrix} 3 & -3 \\ 8 & 0 \\ 7 & 1 \end{bmatrix}$

9. Use the given matrices to evaluate $A(B + C)$.

$$A = \begin{bmatrix} 1 & -6 \\ 2 & 1 \\ 2 & 5 \end{bmatrix}, B = \begin{bmatrix} 0 & -8 \\ 5 & 2 \end{bmatrix}, C = \begin{bmatrix} 1 & 8 \\ -4 & 0 \end{bmatrix}$$

10. A coordinator rents materials for two festivals. The coordinator rents 6 portable toilets, 10 canopy tents, and 80 chairs for the first festival and 10 portable toilets, 15 canopy tents, and 200 chairs for the second festival. Each portable toilet costs $140, each canopy tent costs $60, and each chair costs $2. Use matrix multiplication to find the total rental cost for each festival.

11. An auto dealer needs several tires of different sizes for three types of sedans. The table shows the numbers of each tire size needed. Each 15-inch tire costs $60, each 16-inch tire costs $75, and each 17-inch tire costs $90. Use matrix multiplication to find the total cost of the tires for each type of sedan.

	15-inch	16-inch	17-inch
Compact	12	12	8
Mid-size	4	16	0
Full-size	4	8	8

12.2 Review & Refresh

1. Graph $f(x) = 3 \sin \pi x$.

2. You use technology to simulate rolling a die 75 times. The results are shown in the bar graph. What proportion of the 75 rolls resulted in a number less than 3?

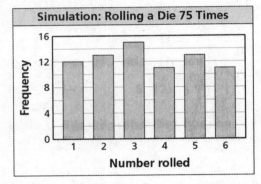

Simulation: Rolling a Die 75 Times

3. You borrow $4000 to buy a boat. The loan has a 6% annual interest rate that is compounded monthly for 5 years. The monthly payment is $77.33. Find the balance after the third payment.

4. Solve $x^2 + 27 = 2$.

5. Consider the infinite geometric series $\frac{1}{3} + \frac{1}{6} + \frac{1}{12} + \frac{1}{24} + \frac{1}{48} + \cdots$. Find and graph the partial sums S_n for $n = 1, 2, 3, 4,$ and 5. Then describe what happens to S_n as n increases.

In Exercises 6 and 7, perform the indicated operation(s).

6. $\begin{bmatrix} 3 & 6 \\ 1 & -4 \end{bmatrix} \begin{bmatrix} -1 & 0 \\ 3 & 5 \end{bmatrix}$

7. $\begin{bmatrix} 1 & -2 \\ 9 & 7 \end{bmatrix} + 2\begin{bmatrix} -1 & 0 \\ 4 & -4 \end{bmatrix}$

8. Let $f(x) = \sqrt{x+1}$ and $g(x) = x^2 - 7$. Find $f(g(3))$.

12.2 Self-Assessment

Use the scale to rate your understanding of the learning target and the success criteria.

1 I do not understand.	2 I can do it with help.	3 I can do it on my own.	4 I can teach someone else.

	Rating	Date
12.2 Multiplying Matrices		
Learning Target: Understand how to multiply matrices.	1 2 3 4	
I can determine whether a product of matrices is defined.	1 2 3 4	
I can multiply matrices.	1 2 3 4	
I can use matrix multiplication to solve real-life problems.	1 2 3 4	

12.3 Extra Practice

In Exercises 1–4, evaluate the determinant of the matrix.

1. $\begin{bmatrix} 5 & 3 \\ 4 & 6 \end{bmatrix}$

2. $\begin{bmatrix} -1 & 3 \\ -9 & 8 \end{bmatrix}$

3. $\begin{bmatrix} -1 & 0 & 3 \\ 5 & 6 & -2 \\ -4 & 1 & 8 \end{bmatrix}$

4. $\begin{bmatrix} 7 & -1 & 4 \\ 1 & -2 & -2 \\ -4 & -5 & 0 \end{bmatrix}$

In Exercises 5 and 6, find the area of the triangle.

5.

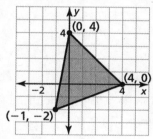

6.

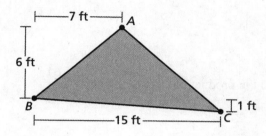

In Exercises 7–10, use Cramer's Rule to solve the linear system.

7. $2x + y = -8$
   $3x - y = -7$

8. $3x - 2y = -1$
   $-x + 5y = 9$

9. $3x + y + z = 11$
   $5x - 2y + 2z = 18$
   $-2x + 3y + z = -9$

10. $x + y + 3z = 1$
    $-6x + 3y - 2z = -13$
    $8x - z = 25$

11. There are x unsigned and y signed books sold at an event. The cost of an unsigned book is $20 and the cost of a signed book is $30. The total revenue from selling 22 books is $580. Write and solve a system to determine the number of books of each type sold at the event.

12.3   Review & Refresh

1. Graph $g(x) = (x - 1)(x + 1)$. Identify the x-intercepts and the points where the local maximums and local minimums occur. Determine the intervals for which the function is increasing or decreasing.

2. Solve the equation for a, b, c, and d.

$$\begin{bmatrix} 4 + a & -3b \\ c & 1 - d \end{bmatrix} = \begin{bmatrix} 5 & 9 \\ 11 & -4 \end{bmatrix}$$

3. Find the product of $\begin{bmatrix} 1 & -4 \\ 6 & 0 \end{bmatrix}$ and $\begin{bmatrix} 2 & 6 \\ 5 & 1 \end{bmatrix}$.

4. Use Cramer's Rule to solve the system.

$$2x + 5y = 2$$
$$-3x + y = 14$$

5. Find all the real zeros of
$f(x) = x^3 + 4x^2 - 11x + 6$.

6. Verify the identity $2 \cos x \tan x \csc x = 2$.

7. You have four green lures and six red lures. You randomly select a lure, set it aside, and then randomly select another lure. Determine whether randomly selecting a green lure first and a red lure second are independent events.

8. Find the inverse of the function $f(x) = 16x^2$, $x \geq 0$. Then graph the function and its inverse.

9. Graph the function $y = e^{x-1}$. Then find the domain and range.

10. Find the sum of $\dfrac{1}{x + 3}$ and $\dfrac{2x}{x + 2}$.

12.3   Self-Assessment

Use the scale to rate your understanding of the learning target and the success criteria.

1 I do not understand.	**2** I can do it with help.	**3** I can do it on my own.	**4** I can teach someone else.

	Rating	Date
12.3 Determinants and Cramer's Rule		
Learning Target: Find and use determinants of matrices.	1 2 3 4	
I can find the determinant of a square matrix.	1 2 3 4	
I can use determinants to find areas of triangles.	1 2 3 4	
I can use determinants to solve systems of equations.	1 2 3 4	

12.4 Extra Practice

In Exercises 1 and 2, find the inverse of the matrix.

1. $\begin{bmatrix} 3 & 5 \\ 5 & 8 \end{bmatrix}$

2. $\begin{bmatrix} -4 & -6 \\ 7 & 10 \end{bmatrix}$

In Exercises 3 and 4, solve the matrix equation.

3. $\begin{bmatrix} 3 & 5 \\ 1 & 2 \end{bmatrix} X = \begin{bmatrix} -2 & -4 \\ 7 & 1 \end{bmatrix}$

4. $\begin{bmatrix} -3 & 14 \\ -2 & 10 \end{bmatrix} X = \begin{bmatrix} 6 & 10 \\ -7 & 4 \end{bmatrix}$

In Exercises 5 and 6, use technology to find the inverse of A. Then use technology to verify your result.

5. $A = \begin{bmatrix} 1 & 1 & -1 \\ 2 & 0 & 1 \\ 4 & 1 & 0 \end{bmatrix}$

6. $A = \begin{bmatrix} 2 & 0 & -1 \\ -3 & -2 & 0 \\ -1 & -1 & 1 \end{bmatrix}$

In Exercises 7 and 8, use an inverse matrix to solve the linear system.

7. $x - 2y = 4$
   $x + y = 10$

8. $-3x + 5y = -14$
   $2x - y = 0$

9. A company sells three sizes of vegetable platters as shown. What is the cost of each type of vegetable?

Small platter 3^{78}
Contains 4 carrots, 3 celery sticks, and 2 peppers

Medium platter 5^{77}
Contains 6 carrots, 5 celery sticks, and 3 peppers

Large platter 8^{71}
Contains 8 carrots, 7 celery sticks, and 5 peppers

12.4 Review & Refresh

In Exercises 1 and 2, factor the polynomial completely.

1. $16x^2 - 49$

2. $3x^5 - 4x^4 + x^3$

3. The table shows the child and adult enrollment in an event by experience level for 2010 and 2020. Organize the information using two matrices, one for 2010 and one for 2020. Then find and interpret a matrix that gives the change in enrollment for each group from 2010 to 2020.

Enrollment

Level	Children 2010	Children 2020	Adults 2010	Adults 2020
Level 1	21	25	22	25
Level 2	14	15	8	10
Level 3	2	5	14	15

4. Evaluate $\csc \dfrac{\pi}{6}$ without using technology.

5. Use the given matrices to evaluate $B(A + C)$.

$$A = \begin{bmatrix} -2 & 4 \\ 1 & 5 \end{bmatrix}, B = \begin{bmatrix} 1 & -2 \\ 0 & -2 \\ 8 & 0 \end{bmatrix}, C = \begin{bmatrix} 7 & -1 \\ -1 & 1 \end{bmatrix}$$

6. Use an inverse matrix to solve the linear system.

$$-2x + 5y = 32$$
$$x - 3y = -19$$

7. The shaded region represents 34% of the area under a normal curve. What are the mean and standard deviation of the normal distribution?

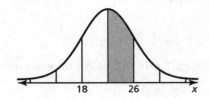

8. Solve $-\dfrac{1}{8}(x - 2)^2 = -8$.

12.4 Self-Assessment

Use the scale to rate your understanding of the learning target and the success criteria.

1 I do not understand.	**2** I can do it with help.	**3** I can do it on my own.	**4** I can teach someone else.

	Rating	Date
12.4 Inverse Matrices		
Learning Target: Understand the relationship between a matrix and its inverse.	1 2 3 4	
I can find the inverse of a matrix.	1 2 3 4	
I can solve linear systems using inverse matrices.	1 2 3 4	
I can solve real-life problems using inverse matrices.	1 2 3 4	

Name_____ Date_____

Chapter 12 — Chapter Self-Assessment

Use the scale to rate your understanding of the learning target and the success criteria.

1 I do not understand. **2** I can do it with help. **3** I can do it on my own. **4** I can teach someone else.

	Rating	Date
Chapter 12 Matrices		
Learning Target: Understand matrices.	1 2 3 4	
I can perform operations with matrices.	1 2 3 4	
I can determine when a product of matrices is defined.	1 2 3 4	
I can evaluate determinants of matrices.	1 2 3 4	
I can use inverse matrices to solve problems.	1 2 3 4	
12.1 Basic Matrix Operations		
Learning Target: Perform basic operations involving matrices.	1 2 3 4	
I can add and subtract matrices.	1 2 3 4	
I can multiply matrices by scalars.	1 2 3 4	
I can solve matrix equations.	1 2 3 4	
I can represent data in a matrix to solve real-life problems.	1 2 3 4	
12.2 Multiplying Matrices		
Learning Target: Understand how to multiply matrices.	1 2 3 4	
I can determine whether a product of matrices is defined.	1 2 3 4	
I can multiply matrices.	1 2 3 4	
I can use matrix multiplication to solve real-life problems.	1 2 3 4	
12.3 Determinants and Cramer's Rule		
Learning Target: Find and use determinants of matrices.	1 2 3 4	
I can find the determinant of a square matrix.	1 2 3 4	
I can use determinants to find areas of triangles.	1 2 3 4	
I can use determinants to solve systems of equations.	1 2 3 4	

Chapter 12 Chapter Self-Assessment (continued)

	Rating	Date
12.4 Inverse Matrices		
Learning Target: Understand the relationship between a matrix and its inverse.	1 2 3 4	
I can find the inverse of a matrix.	1 2 3 4	
I can solve linear systems using inverse matrices.	1 2 3 4	
I can solve real-life problems using inverse matrices.	1 2 3 4	

Chapter 12 Test Prep

1. Which statement about the product AB is true?

$$A = \begin{bmatrix} 1 & 2 & 6 \\ 0 & 3 & 2 \end{bmatrix} \text{ and } B = \begin{bmatrix} 1 & 5 \\ 3 & 0 \\ 3 & 2 \end{bmatrix}$$

Ⓐ The product AB is not defined.

Ⓑ The product AB is defined and is a 2×2 matrix with all positive elements.

Ⓒ The product AB is defined and is a 3×2 matrix with all negative elements.

Ⓓ The product AB is defined and is a 2×3 matrix with all nonnegative elements.

2. A spinner is divided into equal parts. Find the probability that you get a number less than 3 on your first spin and an even number on your second spin. Let event A be "less than 3 on first spin" and let event B be "even number on second spin." Give your answer as a decimal.

$P(A \text{ and } B) =$

3. One term of a geometric sequence is $a_{10} = 750$. The common ratio is 0.1. What is another term of the sequence?

Ⓐ $a_7 = 0.075$

Ⓑ $a_8 = 750{,}000$

Ⓒ $a_{12} = 75{,}000$

Ⓓ $a_{13} = 0.75$

4. For what value of k is the determinant of

$$\begin{bmatrix} 5 & -1 \\ k^2 & k \end{bmatrix} \text{ equal to 6?}$$

Ⓐ $k = -1$

Ⓑ $k = 0$

Ⓒ $k = 1$

Ⓓ $k = 6$

Chapter 12 Test Prep (continued)

5. Which value is the greatest?

$$\begin{bmatrix} a-1 & 4 \\ b & 9 \end{bmatrix} = \begin{bmatrix} -3 & c+4 \\ 6 & -d \end{bmatrix}$$

(A) a

(B) b

(C) c

(D) d

6. Find the area of the triangle.

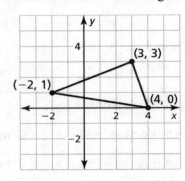

_____ square units

7. The function $C(x) = 20x + 50$ represents the cost (in dollars) of producing x specialized lapel pins. The number of pins produced in t minutes is represented by $x(t) = 2t$. Evaluate $C(x(3))$ and explain what it represents.

(A) $C(x(3)) = 110$; It represents the number of pins produced in 3 minutes.

(B) $C(x(3)) = 170$; It represents the number of pins produced in 6 minutes.

(C) $C(x(3)) = 110$; It represents the cost to produce 3 pins.

(D) $C(x(3)) = 170$; It represents the cost to produce 6 pins.

8. Let the graph of g be a vertical stretch by a factor of 3, followed by a translation 2 units up of the graph of $f(x) = x^2$. Which of the following is an equation for $g(x)$?

(A) $g(x) = 3x^2 + 2$

(B) $g(x) = 2x^2 + 3$

(C) $g(x) = 9x^2 + 2$

(D) $g(x) = \frac{1}{3}x^2 + 2$

Chapter 12 **Test Prep** (continued)

9. Select all the matrices for which the inverse is defined.

Ⓐ $\begin{bmatrix} 4 & -2 \\ 7 & 6 \end{bmatrix}$

Ⓑ $\begin{bmatrix} 1 & 3 \\ 2 & 6 \end{bmatrix}$

Ⓒ $\begin{bmatrix} 8 & -4 \\ 4 & 2 \end{bmatrix}$

Ⓓ $\begin{bmatrix} -1 & 5 \\ -1 & 0 \end{bmatrix}$

10. Which equation represents the parabola?

Ⓐ $f(x) = -\frac{1}{16}x^2$

Ⓑ $f(x) = -\frac{1}{4}x^2 + 2$

Ⓒ $f(x) = 4 - \frac{1}{8}x^2$

Ⓓ $f(x) = -\frac{1}{8}x^2 + 2$

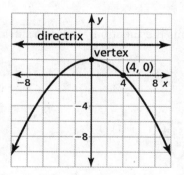

11. The students in two classes submit apparel choices for an upcoming homecoming parade. The matrix on the left represents the number of each apparel item ordered for each class. The matrix on the right represents the cost of each apparel item. Find the total cost of apparel for Class A.

Apparel Selection

	Beanie	Shirt	Hoodie
Class A	10	4	12
Class B	10	6	9

Cost

Dollars

Beanie	9
Shirt	15
Hoodie	20

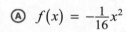

Chapter 12 Test Prep (continued)

12. The area of a rectangle is 50 square units. The length of the rectangle is $(x + 7)$ units and the width is $(x + 2)$ units. Find x.

Ⓐ $x = -12$

Ⓑ $x = -3$

Ⓒ $x = 3$

Ⓓ $x = 12$

13. Select all expressions that are equivalent to $4 \ln x - 3 \ln 2$.

Ⓐ $\ln \dfrac{x^4}{8}$

Ⓑ $\dfrac{4}{3} \ln x^2$

Ⓒ $\ln x^4 - \ln 8$

Ⓓ $\dfrac{\ln x^4}{\ln 8}$

Ⓔ $\ln(x^4 - 8)$

14. Which graph represents the function $f(x) = 5 \sin(x - \pi)$?

Ⓐ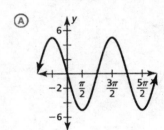

Ⓑ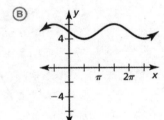

Ⓒ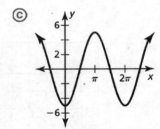

Ⓓ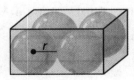

15. Four spherical oranges fit tightly into a gift box. Find the percent of the volume of the box that is occupied by the oranges. Use 3.14 for π and round your answer to the nearest tenth of a percent.

_____

Name_____ Date _____

Algebra 2 — Post-Course Test

1. Find $\left(\dfrac{f}{g}\right)(2)$ given that $f(x) = -10x$ and $g(x) = x + 3$.

2. Solve $2\sqrt[3]{5x + 2} = 4$.

$x =$

3. Which of the following correctly orders $e^{\ln 4}$, $\log_2 2^6$, $\log_2 33$, and $\log_3 26$ from least value to greatest value?

(A) $e^{\ln 4}$, $\log_2 2^6$, $\log_2 33$, $\log_3 26$

(B) $\log_2 33$, $e^{\ln 4}$, $\log_2 2^6$, $\log_3 26$

(C) $\log_3 26$, $e^{\ln 4}$, $\log_2 33$, $\log_2 2^6$

(D) $\log_2 2^6$, $\log_3 26$, $e^{\ln 4}$, $\log_2 33$, $e^{\ln 4}$

4. The product of two binomials is $x^2 + 12x - 13$. What is the sum of the two binomials?

(A) $2x - 12$

(B) $2x + 12$

(C) $2x + 2\sqrt{13}$

(D) $2x - 14$

5. What is the LCD of the rational expressions in $\dfrac{6}{x} + \dfrac{1}{x + 2} = \dfrac{3}{x}$?

(A) x

(B) $x + 2$

(C) $x(x + 2)$

(D) $x^2(x + 2)$

Algebra 2 **Post-Course Test** (continued)

6. Which graph represents the function $f(x) = 1 - \left(\dfrac{1}{2}\right)^x$?

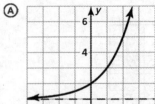 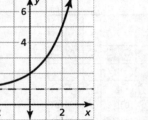

Ⓐ

Ⓑ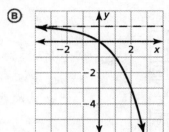

Ⓒ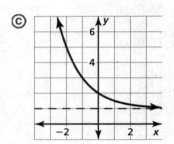

Ⓓ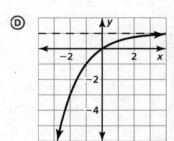

7. Write an equation of the parabola in vertex form that passes through (−2, 4) and has a vertex of (0, 8).

_____

8. What is the vertex of

$f(x) = 2(x - 3)^2 + 7$?

  Ⓐ (−3, −7)

  Ⓑ (−3, 7)

  Ⓒ (3, −7)

  Ⓓ (3, 7)

9. Which degree measure is equivalent to $\dfrac{3\pi}{8}$?

  Ⓐ 22.5°

  Ⓑ 67.5°

  Ⓒ 135°

  Ⓓ 225°

10. At a school, 16% of students participate in a regional competition, 5% of students participate in a state competition, and 2% of students participate in both a regional and a state competition. What is the probability that a student who participates in a regional competition also participates in a state competition?

Ⓐ 0.8%

Ⓑ 3.2%

Ⓒ 12.5%

Ⓓ 40%

11. Which graph represents the function $f(x) = \dfrac{1}{x-2} + 2$?

Ⓐ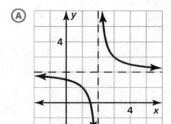

Ⓑ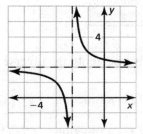

Ⓒ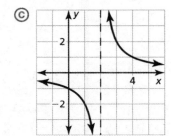

Ⓓ

12. What is the greatest number of real zeros for a polynomial function of degree 4?

Ⓐ 1

Ⓑ 2

Ⓒ 3

Ⓓ 4

13. Which of the following represents $3x^3 - 12xy^2$ factored completely?

Ⓐ $3x(x^2 - 4y^2)$

Ⓑ $3x(x + 2y)(x - 2y)$

Ⓒ $3x(2y + x)(2y - x)$

Ⓓ $3(x + 4y)(x - 4y)$

Algebra 2 **Post-Course Test** (continued)

14. Solve $1 = \sqrt{2} \sin(x + 90°)$
for $0 \leq x \leq 90°$.

15. Write the expression $\sqrt{2} \cdot \sqrt{49} \cdot \sqrt{2}$
in simplest form.

$x = $ [grid-in answer box] °

[grid-in answer box]

16. Which statement is true about the inverse of $f(x) = 2x - 4$?

Ⓐ The inverse of f is a function; $f^{-1}(x) = \dfrac{1}{2}x + 2$.

Ⓑ The inverse of f is a function; $f^{-1}(x) = 2x + 4$.

Ⓒ The inverse of f is not a function; $f^{-1}(x) = \dfrac{1}{2}x + 2$.

Ⓓ The inverse of f is not a function; $f^{-1}(x) = 2x + 4$.

17. Which statement about the graph of the function g is true?

Ⓐ The degree is even and the leading coefficient is positive.

Ⓑ The degree is odd and the leading coefficient is positive.

Ⓒ The degree is even and the leading coefficient is negative.

Ⓓ The degree is odd and the leading coefficient is negative.

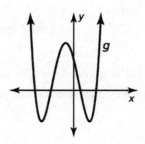

Algebra 2 **Post-Course Test** (continued)

18. For which sequence is the sum of the first three terms equal to 60?

    (A) $a_n = 10 + 6n$

    (B) $a_n = 18 + n$

    (C) $a_n = 8^n - 4$

    (D) $a_n = \frac{1}{2}(4)^n$

19. Which equation represents a line through the points (0, 4) and (2, 0)?

    (A) $y = x - 2$

    (B) $y = 2x + 4$

    (C) $y = 4x - 2$

    (D) $y = -2x + 4$

20. What is the range of $y = -2x^2$?

    (A) All real numbers

    (B) $y < 0$

    (C) $y \le 0$

    (D) $y \le -2$

21. Which point is a solution of $y < x^2 + 6x + 8$?

    (A) (−3, 10)

    (B) (−3, 5)

    (C) (−3, −1)

    (D) (−3, −5)

22. Nine students are competing in an art show. In how many ways can the students finish first and second?

    (A) 18

    (B) 36

    (C) 72

    (D) 181,440

23. You want to determine whether students in your school like the new vending machines. You randomly select 20 students from each grade. Which type of sample did you use?

    (A) systematic sample

    (B) stratified sample

    (C) cluster sample

    (D) convenience sample

Algebra 2

Post-Course Test (continued)

24. What is the ratio of the perimeter to the area of the rectangle shown?

Ⓐ $\dfrac{3x + 7}{x^2 + 5x + 6}$

Ⓑ $\dfrac{2x^2 + 10x + 12}{6x + 14}$

Ⓒ $\dfrac{3x + 7}{2x^2 + 10x + 12}$

Ⓓ $\dfrac{1}{x + 3}$

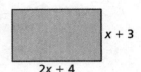

x + 3

2x + 4

25. What are the zeros of
$f(x) = 3x^2 + 21$?

Ⓐ $x = -\sqrt{7}$ and $x = \sqrt{7}$

Ⓑ $x = -\sqrt{3}$ and $x = \sqrt{3}$

Ⓒ $x = -i\sqrt{7}$ and $x = i\sqrt{7}$

Ⓓ $x = -i\sqrt{3}$ and $x = i\sqrt{3}$

26. Select all the equations such that x and y show direct variation.

Ⓐ $-xy = 4$

Ⓑ $x = -y$

Ⓒ $x + 2 = y$

Ⓓ $3x = y$

27. Evaluate $\sin \dfrac{\pi}{2} - 5\cos \dfrac{\pi}{3}$.
Write your answer as a decimal.

28. Which matrix has the same determinant
as $\begin{bmatrix} 2 & k \\ 3 & -2 \end{bmatrix}$?

Ⓐ $\begin{bmatrix} -4 & k \\ 3 & 0 \end{bmatrix}$

Ⓑ $\begin{bmatrix} k & -2 \\ 2 & -3 \end{bmatrix}$

Ⓒ $\begin{bmatrix} k & 1 \\ 4 & -3 \end{bmatrix}$

Ⓓ $\begin{bmatrix} -3 & -2 \\ 2 & -k \end{bmatrix}$

Algebra 2

Post-Course Test (continued)

29. A journalist surveys urban residents and rural residents at random about their opinion of a bill. The two-way table shows the results. Select all the true statements about the two-way table.

		Opinion	
		Positive	Negative
Type of Resident	Rural	20	5
	Urban	12	13

(A) Fifty residents were surveyed.

(B) Of urban residents, 48% have a negative opinion.

(C) Of those who have a positive opinion, 12 are urban residents.

(D) Of those who have a positive opinion, 80% are rural residents.

(E) 80% of the rural residents have a positive opinion.

30. The graph of a function is shown. Select all the equations that represent the graph.

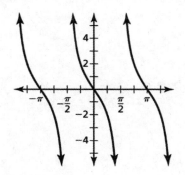

(A) $f(x) = -2\tan(x + \pi)$

(B) $f(x) = 2\tan(x - \pi)$

(C) $f(x) = \tan(x + 2\pi)$

(D) $f(x) = 2\cot\left(x - \frac{\pi}{2}\right)$

(E) $f(x) = \cot(x - 2\pi)$

(F) $f(x) = -2\cot(x + \pi)$

31. The lengths of lip-synching videos on a website are normally distributed with a mean of 20 seconds and a standard deviation of 5 seconds. What percent of videos on the website are between 15 and 25 seconds long?

(A) about 16%

(B) about 34%

(C) about 68%

(D) about 95%

Algebra 2

Post-Course Test (continued)

32. Select all the expressions equivalent to $\left(\sqrt[4]{16}\right)^3$.

- Ⓐ 6
- Ⓑ $16^{3/4}$
- Ⓒ 8
- Ⓓ $16^{4/3}$

33. What is the first term of a geometric sequence with a common ratio of -2 and $a_5 = -80$?

- Ⓐ -1280
- Ⓑ -5
- Ⓒ 5
- Ⓓ 1280

34. Write the series $5 + 9 + 13 + 17 + 21$ using summation notation.

_____

35. Simplify $e^x \cdot e^{-3} \cdot e^{x+6}$.

_____

36. Solve $4^{x+1} = 16^{x-4}$.

$x =$

37. The numbers of apps of 20 tablet owners are shown in the table. Find the sample mean $\overline{x}$.

$\overline{x} =$

Number of Apps	
10	12
13	9
14	14
12	10
8	15
14	14
12	16
17	20
25	26
18	21

Algebra 2 Post-Course Test (continued)

38. What is the amplitude of the function $y = a \sin bx$?

_____

39. Which of the following describes the transformation of $f(x) = e^x$ represented by $g(x) = e^{-x+1}$?

(A) The graph of g is a horizontal translation 1 unit left of the graph of f.

(B) The graph of g is a reflection in the y-axis followed by a horizontal translation 1 unit right of the graph of f.

(C) The graph of g is a reflection in the x-axis followed by a horizontal translation 1 unit right of the graph of f.

(D) The graph of g is a reflection in the line $y = -x + 1$ of the graph of f.

40. A cornhole bag is tossed from 3 feet above the ground, and its height h (in feet) can be modeled by $h(t) = -16t^2 + 16t + 3$, where t is the time (in seconds) after the bag is tossed. What is the maximum height of the bag?

41. Select all the factors of $2x^3 + 7x^2 + 2x - 3$.

(A) $x - 1$

(B) $x + 1$

(C) $x - 3$

(D) $x + 3$

(E) $2x + 1$

(F) $2x - 1$

Algebra 2 **Post-Course Test** (continued)

42. Which function represents exponential growth?

   Ⓐ $y = 2(0.75)^x$

   Ⓑ $y = (1.25)^x$

   Ⓒ $y = 0.25(0.05)^x$

   Ⓓ $y = -\left(\frac{e}{4}\right)^x$

43. What is $f(g(x))$ given that $f(x) = -2x$ and $g(x) = 3|x|$?

   Ⓐ $f(g(x)) = 6|x|$

   Ⓑ $f(g(x)) = -6|x|$

   Ⓒ $f(g(x)) = 6x^2$

   Ⓓ $f(g(x)) = -6x^2$

44. The probability of the *complement* of an event is 25%. Describe the probability of the event.

   Ⓐ The probability of the event is 75%. So, the event is likely to happen.

   Ⓑ The probability of the event is 25%. So, the event is unlikely to happen.

   Ⓒ The probability of the event is 75%. So, the event is unlikely to happen.

   Ⓓ The probability of the event is 25%. So, the event is likely to happen.

45. The function $V(x) = \frac{4}{3}\pi x^3$ represents the volume (in cubic feet) of the sphere. The function $W(x) = V(3x)$ represents the volume (in cubic feet) of the sphere when x is measured in yards. Find $W(2)$. Use 3.14 for π.

cubic feet

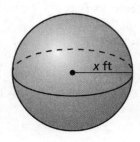

x ft